BELLWORK®

Reading/Language Arts

Level 6

Author
Anne Gall

Contributing Author
Michelle N. Barnett

Editorial Consultants:
Kent A. De Pue
Carrie Hernandez
Erica Kaiser
Margaret Kinney

Illustrator
José L. de la Rosa

The publisher wishes to thank the following educators who read portions of the series prior to publication for their comments and suggestions.

Rebecca Afghani
Linda Behrens
Pam Bluestein
Amy Brophy
Sue Buttera
Mary Johnson Cajiao
Mark Cohen
Marne Colby
Erika Daniels
Carey Davis

Ann DePierro
Victor Dorff
Don Felton
Kim Fortune
Robin Harbeck
Sheri Joseph
Rebecca Keene
Mia Lewis
Sarah Milam
Dennis Regus

Lauren Rips
Ona L. Sandi
Mindi Shapiro
Lynne Shisbey
Ruthie Smith
Kim Marra Stephenson
Kathy Terndrup
Alicia Trent
Jennifer Williams

Copyright © 1991, 1993, 1998, 2004, 2005 BELLWORK Enterprises

BELLWORK
10529 Dale Street
PO Box 205
Stanton, CA 90680-0205

(800) 782-8869
Fax (714) 995-1181
www.bellwork.com

Printed in the U.S.A.
ISBN 1-932469-26-5

Name _____

Choose the answer that will form a complete sentence.

❶ _____ **fell from the swing and hurt her arm.**

- Ⓐ Linda
- Ⓑ On the playground
- Ⓒ Swinging too high
- Ⓓ Last Thursday

❷ _____ **went to the store.**

- Ⓕ On the corner
- Ⓖ After school
- Ⓗ Jeremy and I
- Ⓙ Because we needed milk

❸ _____ **taught us to play football.**

- Ⓐ In the stadium
- Ⓑ The coach
- Ⓒ After learning to play baseball
- Ⓓ Every day during P.E.

❹ _____ **climbed above the clouds.**

- Ⓕ Into the sky
- Ⓖ During the storm
- Ⓗ The powerful jet
- Ⓙ With a huge roar

Name _____

Read each sentence and look at the <u>underlined words</u>. There may be a mistake in them.
Select the best answer to correct the mistake. If there is no mistake, select *correct as is*.

❶ <u>Bob lock the front door</u> when he left the house.

Ⓐ Bob locks the front door

Ⓑ Bob locked the front door

Ⓒ Bob is locking the front door

Ⓓ correct as is

❷ <u>Those cookies was smelling</u> delicious!

Ⓕ Those cookies smell

Ⓖ Those cookies smells

Ⓗ Those cookies is smelling

Ⓘ correct as is

❸ <u>Joanne were talking on the phone</u> for over an hour.

Ⓐ Joanne talk on the phone

Ⓑ Joanne have talked on the phone

Ⓒ Joanne talked on the phone

Ⓓ correct as is

❹ <u>I mowed</u> the lawn today.

Ⓕ I mowing

Ⓖ I has mowed

Ⓗ I is mowing

Ⓘ correct as is

Name _____

Read each set of sentences and decide if one of the <u>underlined words</u> is spelled incorrectly, or if there is *no mistake*. Choose your answer and fill in the bubble.

❶

- Ⓐ Many <u>trees</u> grow in the forest.
- Ⓑ The teacher <u>reviewed</u> the lesson.
- Ⓒ It was dark in the <u>tonnel</u>.
- Ⓓ no mistake

❷

- Ⓕ The sky is very <u>blew</u> today.
- Ⓖ She lowered the <u>anchor</u> slowly.
- Ⓗ The seat on the <u>aisle</u> was taken.
- Ⓙ no mistake

❸

- Ⓐ The horse galloped <u>quickly</u>.
- Ⓑ It was a <u>dangerus</u> road.
- Ⓒ Our <u>fountain</u> is out of water.
- Ⓓ no mistake

❹

- Ⓕ The book's <u>cover</u> was badly worn.
- Ⓖ We like pizza and <u>spaghetti</u>.
- Ⓗ <u>Enough</u> of that nonsense!
- Ⓙ no mistake

3

Name _____

Fill in the bubble next to the answer that correctly completes each sentence.

❶ All insects have six —

(A) legs;

(B) legs?

(C) legs.

(D) legs!

❷ How many of you rode the bus —

(F) today!

(G) today?

(H) today.

(J) today"

❸ What an exciting ride that —

(A) was;

(B) was'

(C) was?

(D) was!

❹ Our teacher's name is —

(F) Mr Taylor.

(G) Mr. Taylor.

(H) Mr, Taylor.

(J) Mr. Taylor?

4

Name _____

Fill in the bubble next to the word that comes *first* in alphabetical order.

1
- Ⓐ tooth
- Ⓑ sleuth
- Ⓒ uncouth
- Ⓓ booth

2
- Ⓕ category
- Ⓖ catch
- Ⓗ caucus
- Ⓙ cavern

3
- Ⓐ legacy
- Ⓑ legality
- Ⓒ legend
- Ⓓ legion

4
- Ⓕ peaceful
- Ⓖ peaceable
- Ⓗ peace
- Ⓙ peacock

5

Read the passage below. Then answer the questions on the next page. You may look back at this page as you answer the questions.

"Come over to my house after school," Lisa said to Amy.

"I can't. I have to go right home. You know that," answered Amy.

"Well, you could call your mother at work and ask her," suggested Lisa.

"No, I can't call her there except in an emergency," Amy replied.

Lisa argued, "Then don't call her. If she's still at work, she won't know anyway."

Amy wanted to go to Lisa's, but she knew her mother expected her to go <u>straight</u> home, do her homework, and start dinner.

Lisa kept it up. "If you don't come over, I won't be your friend."

Amy thought of an alternate plan. "Maybe I can come on Saturday, Lisa?"

"No," <u>she</u> answered. "If you don't come today, I'll never speak to you again!"

1 **In the last sentence, <u>she</u> refers to —**

Ⓐ Amy.

Ⓑ Lisa.

Ⓒ Amy's mother.

2 **In the passage, <u>straight</u> means —**

Ⓕ not crooked.

Ⓖ honest.

Ⓗ logical.

Ⓚ directly.

3 **Why couldn't Amy call her mother at work?**

Ⓐ Lisa would be mad.

Ⓑ It was not an emergency.

Ⓒ She didn't know the number.

Ⓓ She had to do her homework.

4 **You can tell from this passage that Lisa —**

Ⓕ was not really a good friend.

Ⓖ had a surprise for Amy.

Ⓗ was in the same class as Amy.

Ⓚ was older than Amy.

7

Name _____

Fill in the bubble next to the answer that correctly completes each sentence.

1 We like to see fireworks on the _____.

Ⓐ fourth of July
Ⓑ Fourth of july
Ⓒ fourth of july
Ⓓ Fourth of July

2 A large amount of the United States' gold reserves is stored in the vault of the _____ Bullion Depository.

Ⓕ fort knox
Ⓖ Fort Knox
Ⓗ Fort knox
Ⓙ fort Knox

3 The _____ is the longest river in South America.

Ⓐ Amazon river
Ⓑ amazon river
Ⓒ amazon River
Ⓓ Amazon River

4 My dentist, _____, cleaned my teeth.

Ⓕ dr. Crandall
Ⓖ Dr. Crandall
Ⓗ dr. crandall
Ⓙ Dr. crandall

8

Name _____

Read each sentence and look at the <u>underlined words</u>. There may be a mistake in them. Select the best answer to correct the mistake. If there is no mistake, select *correct as is*.

1 <u>**Those boys speak**</u> **Spanish as well as English.**

   Ⓐ Those boys speaks
   Ⓑ Those boys is speaking
   Ⓒ Those boys was speaking
   Ⓓ correct as is

2 **Mark lives at 3121** <u>**hillview lane.**</u>

   Ⓕ hillview Lane.
   Ⓖ Hillview Lane.
   Ⓗ Hillview lane.
   Ⓙ correct as is

3 **Will you come to my house after** <u>**school?**</u>

   Ⓐ school.
   Ⓑ school,
   Ⓒ school!
   Ⓓ correct as is

4 **Elmas said,** <u>**"i'd like to read this book."**</u>

   Ⓕ "I'd like to read this book.
   Ⓖ I'd like to read this book."
   Ⓗ "I'd like to read this book."
   Ⓙ correct as is

9

Name _____

1 Kelsey saw a black <u>bat</u> in the cave. In this sentence, bat refers to —

Ⓒ the mammal.

Ⓓ the tool.

Ⓔ to bat (*the action word*).

3 Peter wanted to <u>light</u> a fire in the fireplace. In this sentence, light refers to —

Ⓒ the opposite of heavy.

Ⓓ to start burning (*the action word*).

Ⓔ a shaded color.

2 He took a <u>trip</u> to Mexico. In this sentence, trip refers to —

Ⓝ to stumble (*the action word*).

Ⓞ a journey.

Ⓟ something clumsy.

4 My grandmother always <u>checks</u> my homework when I'm done. In this sentence, checks refers to —

Ⓝ the paper money.

Ⓞ the mark (✔).

Ⓟ to verify (*the action word*).

Name _____

Choose the sentence below that combines all of the numbered sentences in the *best*, most concise way.

❶
1. The horse is brown.
2. The horse is powerful.
3. The horse is running.
4. The horse is in the field.

Ⓐ The horse is brown, and powerful, and the horse is running in the field.

Ⓑ The brown and powerful horse, it is running and it is in the field.

Ⓒ The powerful brown horse is running in the field.

Ⓓ The horse is powerful and brown and the horse is running in the field.

❷
1. The ice cream is cold.
2. The ice cream is creamy.
3. The ice cream is chocolate.
4. The ice cream tastes good.

Ⓕ The cold ice cream is creamy and it is chocolate and it tastes good.

Ⓖ The cold, creamy, chocolate ice cream tastes good.

Ⓗ The ice cream that is cold and creamy and chocolate tastes good.

Ⓙ The ice cream tastes good because it is cold and it is creamy and it is chocolate.

11

Read the passage below. Then complete the web organizer on the next page. You may look back at this page as you complete the organizer.

The Effects of Volcanic Eruptions

After a volcano has erupted, there are many different effects that can happen. During an episode of activity, a volcano displays a distinctive pattern of behavior. Some mild eruptions discharge only steam and other gases, while other eruptions extrude quantities of lava. The most spectacular eruptions consist of violent explosions that blast great amounts of magma. The effects of these eruptions, whether a caldera or a volcanic plug, can be equally fascinating.

The largest and most explosive volcanic eruptions eject tens to hundreds of cubic kilometers of magma, or lava, onto the Earth's surface. When such a large volume of magma is removed from beneath a volcano, the ground can begin to collapse into the emptied space. Because of this, a huge depression, called a caldera, forms on the Earth's surface. Calderas can be more than 25 kilometers in diameter and several kilometers deep. Calderas are among the most spectacular volcanic effects on Earth. Beneath a caldera there is interaction of the magma, ground water, and stress in the Earth's crust which can cause earthquakes, geysers, boiling mud pots, and hot springs. The word caldera comes from the Spanish word for kettle or cauldron. The depression is steep and bowl-shaped looking very similar to that of a cauldron.

Another effect of volcanic eruptions is called volcanic plugs or necks. These plugs are formed when the magma solidifies in the pipe of a volcano. Over time, the volcanic rock wears away, leaving behind a solidified "plug." They may be visualized as the fossil remains of the innards of a volcano. One of the best known volcanic plugs, which is more than 1,700 feet above its surrounding plains, can be found in New Mexico. There are other volcanic plugs in the western United States and also in Germany, South Africa, Tanzania, and Siberia.

12

Name _____

Effects of Volcanic Eruptions

calderas

1

Earthquakes, geysers, boiling mud pots, and hot springs can occur from the formation of a caldera.

volcanic plugs

The volcanic rock wears away leaving behind a solidified plug.

2

❶

Ⓐ Calderas can be up to 1,700 feet above the surrounding plains.

Ⓑ Calderas are formed when the ground from the volcano collapses into the empty space.

Ⓒ A caldera is a tall mountain of solidified magma.

❷

Ⓕ The largest volcanic plug can be measured at 25 kilometers in diameter.

Ⓖ Volcanic plugs come from the Spanish word for kettle.

Ⓗ They can be visualized as the fossil remains of a volcano.

Fill in the bubble next to the answer that correctly completes each sentence.

1 Cheryl and I _____ our bikes to the park yesterday.

  Ⓐ ride
  Ⓑ rode
  Ⓒ riding
  Ⓓ rided

2 The glass and plate will _____ if you drop them.

  Ⓕ break
  Ⓖ broke
  Ⓗ breaking
  Ⓙ broken

3 John and I were _____ our favorite song.

  Ⓐ sing
  Ⓑ sang
  Ⓒ singed
  Ⓓ singing

4 Melinda and Jen _____ in the back of the room.

  Ⓕ sitted
  Ⓖ sitting
  Ⓗ sat
  Ⓙ have sit

Name _____

Read each sentence and look at the <u>underlined words</u>. There may be a mistake in them. Select the best answer to correct the mistake. If there is no mistake, select *correct as is*.

❶ <u>Tom hasnt' finished</u> his science project.

 Ⓐ Tom hasn't finished
 Ⓑ Tom has'nt finished
 Ⓒ Tom hasen't finished
 Ⓓ correct as is

❷ Sue said <u>shed' be a little late</u>.

 Ⓕ sheed be a little late
 Ⓖ sh'ed be a little late
 Ⓗ she'd be a little late
 Ⓙ correct as is

❸ <u>I can't find my</u> other shoe.

 Ⓐ I cann't find my
 Ⓑ I ca'nt find my
 Ⓒ I canot find my
 Ⓓ correct as is

❹ <u>It does'nt matter</u> where you sit.

 Ⓕ It doesn't matter
 Ⓖ It doe'snt matter
 Ⓗ It doesnt matter
 Ⓙ correct as is

15

Name _____

Read each sentence and look at the <u>underlined words</u>. There may be a mistake in them. Select the best answer to correct the mistake. If there is no mistake, select *correct as is*.

1 The policeman talked to <u>Dad and I</u>.

   Ⓐ Dad and me
   Ⓑ Dad and she
   Ⓒ Dad and he
   Ⓓ correct as is

2 <u>They helped Jenny</u> clean her room.

   Ⓕ Me helped Jenny
   Ⓖ Her helped Jenny
   Ⓗ Them helped Jenny
   Ⓙ correct as is

3 <u>Us read</u> the best story!

   Ⓐ Him read
   Ⓑ We read
   Ⓒ Her read
   Ⓓ correct as is

4 The principal <u>spoke to she</u> on the playground.

   Ⓕ spoke to we
   Ⓖ spoke to they
   Ⓗ spoke to her
   Ⓙ correct as is

Name _____

Fill in the bubble next to the answer that correctly completes each sentence.

❶ Motoko asked to borrow _____ bike.

Ⓐ Jasons

Ⓑ Jason's

Ⓒ Jasons'

❸ All of my _____ houses are larger than mine.

Ⓐ friends

Ⓑ friends'

Ⓒ friend's

❷ I was surprised at _____ answer.

Ⓕ Marias'

Ⓖ Maria's

Ⓗ Marias

❹ Both _____ fenders were dented.

Ⓕ cars

Ⓖ car's

Ⓗ cars'

17

Name _____

Read each sentence and look at the underlined words. There may be a mistake in them. Select the best answer to correct the mistake. If there is no mistake, select *correct as is*.

1 We <u>saw seven deeries</u> near our campsite one morning.

   Ⓐ saw seven deer

   Ⓑ saw seven deers

   Ⓒ saw seven deeres

   Ⓓ correct as is

2 Our class read a book about <u>president George Bush.</u>

   Ⓕ President George bush.

   Ⓖ President george Bush.

   Ⓗ President George Bush.

   Ⓙ correct as is

3 My parents <u>gaved me permission</u> to go.

   Ⓐ given me permission

   Ⓑ is given me permission

   Ⓒ have given me permission

   Ⓓ correct as is

4 We grew <u>corn, beans, and tomatoes</u> in our garden.

   Ⓕ corn, beans and, tomatoes

   Ⓖ corn beans, and tomatoes

   Ⓗ corn, beans and tomatoes,

   Ⓙ correct as is

18

Name _____

Read each list of words. Fill in the bubble next to the *indefinite pronoun*.

1

Ⓐ the class
Ⓑ everybody
Ⓒ them
Ⓓ 15 people

2

Ⓕ she
Ⓖ Susan
Ⓗ Lauren and Jacob
Ⓙ anyone

3

Ⓐ anything
Ⓑ the chair
Ⓒ those
Ⓓ us

4

Ⓕ a pound
Ⓖ her
Ⓗ those
Ⓙ some

Name _____

Fill in the bubble next to the answer that correctly completes each sentence.

1 To find the name of the author of a book you are reading, you should look —

Ⓐ at the title page.

Ⓑ in the table of contents.

Ⓒ in the glossary.

Ⓓ in the index.

2 To find the meaning of a word in your health book, you should look —

Ⓕ in the table of contents.

Ⓖ in the index.

Ⓗ in the glossary.

Ⓘ at the title page.

3 In your science book, to find the page with information about electricity, you should look —

Ⓐ in the preface.

Ⓑ in the glossary.

Ⓒ in the table of contents.

Ⓓ in the index.

4 To find the page that a story begins in your reading book, you should look —

Ⓕ at the title page.

Ⓖ in the table of contents.

Ⓗ in the glossary.

Ⓘ in the index.

Name _____

❶ Choose the sentence that is the *best* topic sentence (main idea) for this paragraph.

_____ When my puppy was small, he chewed on everything in sight, so we named him "Chewie." He especially loved anything made of leather. Dad's slippers were the first to go, and the corner of mom's briefcase was next. He also chewed the legs on the dining room table. You can see his teeth marks there.

Ⓐ Young puppies need a warm place to sleep.

Ⓑ Young puppies can be very destructive.

Ⓒ Young puppies can be taught to do tricks.

Ⓓ Leather is not good for young puppies.

❷ Choose the sentence for the blank line in the paragraph that *best supports* the topic sentence.

The old house on Elm Street looked spooky. It hadn't been painted in years, and the paint that did remain was fading and peeling. _____ The fence was sagging and broken, and the gate, hanging by one hinge, stood partly open. It seemed as if a ghost might pop out at any moment!

Ⓕ Houses should be painted about every five years to maintain their beauty.

Ⓖ There are only three houses remaining on Elm Street.

Ⓗ The Johnsons used to own the house.

Ⓙ The windows were broken and an old curtain hung partly out of one.

21

Read the passage below. Then answer the questions on the next page. You may look back at this page as you answer the questions.

For many, many years, people have looked up at the birds in the sky and wished that they, too, could fly. There is a mythical story of Daedalus and Icarus, who made wings of wax and feathers with which to fly over their prison walls. Do you know what happened to Icarus? When he failed to follow instructions and flew too near the sun, the wax melted, and he fell into the sea. That was a good story, but in 1680 an Italian mathematician proved that man's arms are too weak to use like wings.

However, man continued to try to imitate birds. By the 1700's, some people had learned to float in balloons which were filled with hot air to make them rise. In the 1800's in both England and Germany, successful <u>motorless</u> gliders made many flights. Before the Wright Brothers flew the first powered plane, they too practiced making and flying gliders.

Today, you can float like a bird in a modern airplane, a glider, or even a hang glider. However, be careful. We don't want you to fall into the sea!

Name _____

1 From this passage, you know that the story of Daedalus and Icarus was —

Ⓐ a fairy tale.

Ⓑ a tall tale.

Ⓒ a myth.

Ⓓ a biography.

2 In the word <u>motorless</u>, the <u>less</u> makes the word mean —

Ⓕ a powerful motor.

Ⓖ without a motor.

Ⓗ with many motors.

Ⓙ one who motors.

3 Which of the following methods of flight came first?

Ⓐ hang gliders

Ⓑ hot air balloons

Ⓒ motorless gliders

Ⓓ powered planes

4 You might *predict* from the passage that —

Ⓕ man will continue to improve methods of flight.

Ⓖ a man in flight will fall into the sea.

Ⓗ a glider will never be invented.

Ⓙ flying will always be dangerous.

23

1 **Our apartment is on the third <u>story</u>. In this sentence, story refers to —**

(A) a fictional narrative.

(B) a novel.

(C) a building level.

2 **My cat always sharpens her claws on the tree <u>bark</u>. In this sentence, bark refers to —**

(F) the sound a dog makes.

(G) the tough covering of a woody stem.

(H) a sailing ship.

3 **Our class <u>lines</u> up behind number 23, our room number. In this sentence, lines refers to —**

(A) a telephone connection.

(B) a string or cord.

(C) to place in a straight form.

4 **There are six <u>bands</u> of color in the rainbow. In this sentence, bands refers to —**

(F) an orchestra.

(G) stripes.

(H) a musical group.

Name _____

Choose the correct pronoun that is needed to fill in the blank.

1 *My aunt and I went shopping at the mall. She wanted to buy a new purse and I wanted to buy a birthday present for my friend, Ronin. We must have been into every store in the mall before she found the purse she was looking for. I had better luck with Ronin's gift. I found the perfect gift for _____ in the very first store!*

Ⓐ she
Ⓑ his
Ⓒ he
Ⓓ him

2 *Amon has never been on a real vacation. His mom works hard, but she has never been able to afford to get away for a week or two. My family is luckier. We usually take a trip every year when school is out. Sometimes we go camping, and sometimes we go to a special city to see the sights. This year, Amon is going with _____ on our vacation.*

Ⓕ she
Ⓖ they
Ⓗ us
Ⓙ we

25

Name _____

Fill in the bubble next to the word (homophone) that correctly completes each sentence.

❶ The ball hit Cara on the _____.

   Ⓐ knows

   Ⓑ nose

❷ _____ shoes got soaked from the rain.

   Ⓕ There

   Ⓖ Their

   Ⓗ They're

❸ We read _____ chapters in our history book.

   Ⓐ to

   Ⓑ two

   Ⓒ too

❹ Tim was wearing a _____ shirt.

   Ⓕ new

   Ⓖ knew

Name _____

Choose the sentence below that combines all of the numbered sentences in the *best*, most concise way.

❶
1. **The snake is a water snake.**
2. **The snake slithered.**
3. **The snake slithered across a rock.**
4. **The snake disappeared into the stream.**

Ⓐ The snake is a water snake, and it slithered across a rock and disappeared into the stream.

Ⓑ The water snake slithered across a rock, and the water snake disappeared into the steam.

Ⓒ The water snake slithered across a rock and disappeared into the stream.

Ⓓ The snake slithered across the water and disappeared behind a rock.

❷
1. **Devak was very tired.**
2. **Devak was afraid he would oversleep.**
3. **Devak set his alarm.**
4. **Devak set his alarm for 6:00.**

Ⓕ Devak was very tired, and he was afraid to oversleep, and he set his alarm for 6:00.

Ⓖ Devak was very tired and would oversleep and set his alarm and he set it for 6:00.

Ⓗ Because Devak was tired, Devak set his alarm for 6:00 so Devak would not oversleep.

Ⓙ Being very tired and afraid he would oversleep, Devak set his alarm for 6:00.

27

Name _____

1 **Fill in the bubble next to the sentence that states a *fact*.**

- Ⓐ France is a country in Europe.
- Ⓑ Blue is the prettiest color.
- Ⓒ Cats are smarter than dogs.
- Ⓓ Football is more exciting than baseball.

2 **Fill in the bubble next to the sentence that states a *fact*.**

- Ⓕ Strawberry ice cream is best.
- Ⓖ Math is harder than English.
- Ⓗ Lightning can start a forest fire.
- Ⓙ Riding a roller coaster is fun.

3 **Fill in the bubble next to the sentence that states an *opinion*.**

- Ⓐ Monday is the day before Tuesday.
- Ⓑ Tennis shoes wear longer than sandals.
- Ⓒ Oranges grow on trees.
- Ⓓ Many people have animals as pets.

4 **Fill in the bubble next to the sentence that states an *opinion*.**

- Ⓕ Pencils are used for writing.
- Ⓖ Mexico is south of the United States.
- Ⓗ A baseball team has nine players.
- Ⓙ Hamburgers are better than hot dogs.

28

Name _____

Read each sentence and look at the <u>underlined words</u>. There may be a mistake in them. Select the best answer to correct the mistake. If there is no mistake, select *correct as is*.

1 **Please help me tie up <u>these newspapers</u> for recycling.**

- Ⓐ this newspapers
- Ⓑ them newspapers
- Ⓒ they newspapers
- Ⓓ correct as is

2 **We visited <u>hoover dam</u>, which is located near Las Vegas, Nevada.**

- Ⓕ Hoover Dam
- Ⓖ hoover Dam
- Ⓗ Hoover dam
- Ⓙ correct as is

3 **<u>Plants needing water</u> in order to grow.**

- Ⓐ Plants is needing water
- Ⓑ Plants need water
- Ⓒ Plants needs water
- Ⓓ correct as is

4 **Father asked, <u>"where are you going?"</u>**

- Ⓕ "Where are you going"
- Ⓖ Where are you going?
- Ⓗ "Where are you going?"
- Ⓙ correct as is

29

Name _____

1 Walk to your nearest branch. Fill out an application. Sign the bottom of the form promising to return all borrowed materials after a certain amount of time. Use the materials that you have checked out and return them by their due date.

This would be the process for obtaining and using which of the following?

Ⓐ bank savings account
Ⓑ public library card
Ⓒ sports club membership
Ⓓ bank checking account

2 Decide which company best suits your needs. Ask details that would be related to your situation. Deposit your money into an account. Choose a design from the sample books. Spend wisely and balance accurately.

This would be the process for owning which of the following?

Ⓕ bank savings account
Ⓖ supermarket card
Ⓗ league membership
Ⓙ bank checking account

Name _____

1 **An exaggerated story is a _____.**

   Ⓐ fairy tale

   Ⓑ tall tale

   Ⓒ myth

   Ⓓ fable

2 **A fictitious story, usually about animals, that is meant to teach a moral lesson is a _____.**

   Ⓕ fairy tale

   Ⓖ tall tale

   Ⓗ myth

   Ⓙ fable

3 **A traditional story serving to explain some phenomenon or custom is a _____.**

   Ⓐ fairy tale

   Ⓑ tall tale

   Ⓒ myth

   Ⓓ fable

4 **A story about fairies and magic deeds is a _____.**

   Ⓕ fairy tale

   Ⓖ tall tale

   Ⓗ myth

   Ⓙ fable

Read the passage below. Then answer the questions on the next page. You may look back at this page as you answer the questions.

"Old people just lie around in nursing homes and complain about their aches and pains."

"All old people are poor."

If you agree with these statements, think again!

Many people, aged sixty or older, are still very healthy and active. They walk, they jog, and play tennis. They dance, exercise, and have fun with their friends, like you do.

Some older persons do have difficulties because their income is limited. However, many who saved for their retirement enjoy traveling to different parts of the world or moving to a new home.

Many of the "<u>elderly</u>" like to learn new things. They take classes to learn how to speak another language or how to do crafts. Some even <u>reenter</u> college and get advanced degrees. Others find new ways to earn money. These active senior citizens continue to earn and learn.

1 In the last paragraph, the term "<u>elderly</u>" means the same as —

Ⓐ limited income.

Ⓑ advanced degrees.

Ⓒ senior citizens.

Ⓓ earn and learn.

2 In the word <u>reenter</u>, the <u>re</u> makes the word mean —

Ⓕ go out of.

Ⓖ enter before.

Ⓗ enter again.

Ⓙ drop out of.

3 What difficulty for senior citizens is mentioned in this passage?

Ⓐ playing tennis

Ⓑ nursing homes

Ⓒ taking classes

Ⓓ limited income

4 You can tell by this passage that the author believes most older people —

Ⓕ enjoy an active, productive life.

Ⓖ are poor.

Ⓗ speak another language.

Ⓙ complain about their aches and pains.

33

Name _____

Read each sentence. Choose the word that best completes the sentence.

1 The children saw _____ bikes being covered with snow.

Ⓐ their

Ⓑ there

Ⓒ they're

2 _____ very happy that the party was a success.

Ⓕ Their

Ⓖ There

Ⓗ They're

3 "I know I put my homework over _____ on the counter," cried Sarah.

Ⓐ their

Ⓑ there

Ⓒ they're

4 The dog chased _____ tail to get attention.

Ⓕ it's

Ⓖ its

Name _____

Fill in the bubble next to the word that correctly completes each sentence.

❶ The diamond ring was very _____.

Ⓐ valuest

Ⓑ valuable

Ⓒ valueness

Ⓓ valuely

❷ Sandra was a _____ worker.

Ⓕ careful

Ⓖ carely

Ⓗ careness

Ⓙ careable

❸ It was a cold and _____ day.

Ⓐ snowful

Ⓑ snowly

Ⓒ snowable

Ⓓ snowy

❹ We thanked the nurse for her _____.

Ⓕ kindly

Ⓖ kindness

Ⓗ kindless

Ⓙ kinder

35

Name _____

Read the student letter, then answer the question.

Dear Sam,

I hope you are feeling better after your operation. I had my tonsils out when I was eight, so I know it isn't fun. The only good part is the ice cream!

Our room beat Room 9 in baseball yesterday. It was a close game. The final score was 4 to 3. Mario knocked in the winning run.

We had an assembly this morning.

Your friend,

Danielle

1 **Suppose your friend just wrote this letter. What advice would help her make it *more* interesting to Sam?**

Ⓐ Don't indent the paragraphs.

Ⓑ Tell Sam how to play baseball.

Ⓒ Add more detail about the assembly.

Ⓓ Danielle should sign her last name.

Name _____

Use the table of contents to answer the questions below.

TABLE OF CONTENTS

Page

The State of California As a Whole 1
How California Came To Be a State 6
The Land of California 11
Coastal and Inland Waters of California 19
California Weather 23
Resources and Industries of California 27
Transportation in California 36

❶ **The chapter most likely to contain information about the fishing industry in California begins on page —**

Ⓐ 6.

Ⓑ 11.

Ⓒ 23.

Ⓓ 27.

❷ **If you want to read about California's Salton Sea, you should start with the chapter that begins on page —**

Ⓕ 11.

Ⓖ 19.

Ⓗ 23.

Ⓙ 36.

Name _____

For each item below, choose the word that means the *same or almost the same* (synonym) as the underlined word.

---

1 a **damp** cloth

- Ⓐ soft
- Ⓑ cold
- Ⓒ wet
- Ⓓ dry

2 a **mean** person

- Ⓕ cruel
- Ⓖ happy
- Ⓗ loud
- Ⓙ thoughtful

3 to **assist** someone

- Ⓐ question
- Ⓑ accompany
- Ⓒ hurt
- Ⓓ help

4 to **inquire** about

- Ⓕ read
- Ⓖ talk
- Ⓗ ask
- Ⓙ listen

Name _____

Choose the word that best connects the thoughts in each of the following sentences.

1 Will you wear your sweater _____ your jacket?

- Ⓐ nor
- Ⓑ yet
- Ⓒ or
- Ⓓ but

2 We ran to catch the bus, _____ we missed it.

- Ⓕ but
- Ⓖ as
- Ⓗ or
- Ⓙ nor

3 Don't start the race _____ I say "go."

- Ⓐ until
- Ⓑ while
- Ⓒ since
- Ⓓ where

4 The car was small _____ powerful.

- Ⓕ because
- Ⓖ nor
- Ⓗ yet
- Ⓙ until

39

Name _____

Fill in the bubble next to the foreign word(s) that correctly complete each sentence.

❶ | Katelyn's mom hired an _____ to care for Katelyn and her brother while she worked.

Which French word/saying correctly fits into the sentence?

Ⓐ au gratin   Ⓒ au jus

Ⓑ au pair   Ⓓ au natural

❷ | _____ means "and so forth." The abbreviation is written "etc."

Which Latin word/saying correctly fits in the sentence?

Ⓕ Ex parte   Ⓗ Et cetera

Ⓖ Et alii   Ⓙ De jure

❸ | After the bell choir's last song, the audience requested an _____. They wanted to hear one more song.

Which French word/saying correctly fits into the sentence?

Ⓐ déjà vu   Ⓒ faux pas

Ⓑ du jour   Ⓓ encore

❹ | Carrie was paid each day for her work. She worked for the company as a _____ employee.

Which Latin word/saying correctly fits into the sentence?

Ⓕ carpe diem   Ⓗ per diem

Ⓖ de facto   Ⓙ ex parte

Name _____

Read each sentence and look at the underlined words. There may be a mistake in them. Select the best answer to correct the mistake. If there is no mistake, select *correct as is*.

1 Kenneth <u>has grew</u> six inches in the last two years.

Ⓐ has grown
Ⓑ has growed
Ⓒ has grow
Ⓓ correct as is

2 The 1984 Summer Olympics were held in <u>Los Angeles, california</u>.

Ⓕ los Angeles, California
Ⓖ Los Angeles, California
Ⓗ Los angeles, California
Ⓙ correct as is

3 <u>These cherries was</u> delicious!

Ⓐ These cherries is
Ⓑ These cherries am
Ⓒ These cherries are
Ⓓ correct as is

4 The door <u>opened slow</u>.

Ⓕ opened slowly
Ⓖ opened slowness
Ⓗ opened slowing
Ⓙ correct as is

41

Name _____

1 Peter Piper picked a peck of
pickled peppers.

The writing technique that uses
repeated consonant sounds is
called —

Ⓐ simile.   Ⓒ hyperbole.

Ⓑ alliteration. Ⓓ personification.

2 My mother is as beautiful as
a rose.

The writing technique that compares
two things using "like" or "as" is
called —

Ⓕ simile.   Ⓗ hyperbole.

Ⓖ alliteration. Ⓙ personification.

3 The rain crept in on little
cat feet.

The writing technique that makes
an inanimate object act like a
person or animal is called —

Ⓐ simile.   Ⓒ hyperbole.

Ⓑ alliteration. Ⓓ personification.

4 My dog is the best dog in the whole
wide world.

The writing technique that uses
exaggeration is called —

Ⓕ simile.   Ⓗ hyperbole.

Ⓖ alliteration. Ⓙ personification.

42

Name _____

1 You want to write about the time your baby brother swallowed a tadpole.

Which form of writing would be the *best* choice?

Ⓐ letter to the editor of your school paper

Ⓑ poem

Ⓒ narrative

Ⓓ review

2 You don't like the school menu because it contains too many high fat foods. You want to share your opinion with the rest of the students at your school.

Which form of writing would be the *best* choice?

Ⓕ letter to the editor of your school paper

Ⓖ poem

Ⓗ narrative

Ⓙ review

43

Read the passage below. Then answer the questions on the next page. You may look back at this page as you answer the questions.

Kids who grow fast may need a new swimsuit each year. Every year, the swimsuits seem to get smaller! Boys swim in trunks or swimming briefs. Girls may wear a form-fitting tank suit or a bikini made of nylon or spandex.

Boys and girls who lived in the 1920's wore "bathing costumes." Boys' "costumes" were made of dark-colored wool. They had a loose, <u>sleeveless</u> top with pants that extended to just above the knees. "Costumes" for girls were usually made of black sateen, a shiny cotton fabric. The top had a blouse with elbow-length sleeves. The bottom consisted of a pleated skirt with matching <u>bloomers</u>. These baggy pants came to just below the knee.

There were very few organized swimming contests for boys, and it was not considered "lady-like" for girls and women to swim in competition. They just "bathed" in the water; thus, the term "bathing suit."

44

Name _____

1 In the word <u>sleeveless</u>, the <u>less</u> makes the word mean —

    Ⓐ without sleeves.

    Ⓑ with sleeves.

    Ⓒ with long sleeves.

    Ⓓ full of sleeves.

2 Whose "bathing costumes" were usually made of wool?

    Ⓕ boys'

    Ⓖ girls'

3 You can tell from this passage that <u>bloomers</u> are —

    Ⓐ sleeveless tops.

    Ⓑ pleated skirts.

    Ⓒ baggy pants.

    Ⓓ swimming contests.

4 In the 1920's, why were there few swimming contests for girls?

    Ⓕ The boys would always win.

    Ⓖ Their costumes were too heavy.

    Ⓗ They were busy bathing.

    Ⓙ It was not considered "lady-like."

45

Name _____

Read each sentence and look at the underlined words. There may be a mistake in them. Select the best answer to correct the mistake. If there is no mistake, select *correct as is*.

1 Mother bought <u>two new dressies</u>.

Ⓐ two new dress

Ⓑ two new dresses

Ⓒ correct as is

2 <u>The strawberry were</u> killed by the frost.

Ⓕ The strawberries were

Ⓖ The strawberrys were

Ⓗ correct as is

3 The storm <u>lasted for five days</u>.

Ⓐ lasted for five day

Ⓑ lasted for five daies

Ⓒ correct as is

4 Matt was <u>invited to two party</u>.

Ⓕ invited to two partys

Ⓖ invited to two parties

Ⓗ correct as is

Name _____

Fill in the bubble next to the word that correctly completes each sentence.

1 Isn't there _____ you want from the market?

 Ⓐ anything

 Ⓑ nothing

2 I don't have _____ time to waste.

 Ⓕ any

 Ⓖ no

3 Haven't you _____ taken a walk in the rain?

 Ⓐ never

 Ⓑ ever

4 Emmanuel just moved and doesn't know _____.

 Ⓕ anyone

 Ⓖ no one

Name _____

Choose the answer that will form a complete sentence.

❶ _____ **went to see the nurse.**

- Ⓐ Because they were sick
- Ⓑ Five sick children
- Ⓒ Not feeling well
- Ⓓ When having chicken pox

❷ _____ **ate a hamburger for lunch.**

- Ⓕ I
- Ⓖ Every Wednesday
- Ⓗ With mustard and pickles
- Ⓙ In the cafeteria

❸ _____ **is singing at the assembly.**

- Ⓐ Having practiced for hours
- Ⓑ With the piano
- Ⓒ The school chorus
- Ⓓ On the stage

❹ _____ **bloomed in the garden.**

- Ⓕ Dropping their leaves
- Ⓖ In straight rows
- Ⓗ Smelling like perfume
- Ⓙ A bright pink rose

Name _____

Choose the sentence below that combines all of the numbered sentences in the *best*, most concise way.

❶
1. **We planted a garden.**
2. **We planted lettuce in our garden.**
3. **We planted squash in our garden.**
4. **We planted tomatoes in our garden.**

Ⓐ In our garden we planted lettuce, and we planted squash and tomatoes.

Ⓑ We planted our garden, and it had lettuce, and it had squash and tomatoes.

Ⓒ We planted lettuce, squash, and tomatoes in our garden.

Ⓓ We planted lettuce, we planted squash, we planted tomatoes in our garden.

❷
1. **We have a dog.**
2. **The dog is our pet.**
3. **Our dog sleeps in a basket.**
4. **The basket is in the kitchen.**

Ⓕ Our dog is a pet, and our pet sleeps in a basket in the kitchen.

Ⓖ Our pet dog sleeps in a basket in the kitchen.

Ⓗ A basket in the kitchen is where our dog, which is a pet, sleeps.

Ⓙ We have a pet dog, and our dog sleeps in a basket in the kitchen.

49

Name _____

Read each sentence and look at the <u>underlined words</u>. There may be a mistake in them. Select the best answer to correct the mistake. If there is no mistake, select *correct as is*.

❶ <u>**Elizabeth is jumped down**</u> **from the step.**

    Ⓐ Elizabeth jumping down
    Ⓑ Elizabeth were jumping down
    Ⓒ Elizabeth jumped down
    Ⓓ correct as is

❷ <u>**Many deer was living**</u> **in the forest.**

    Ⓕ Many deer live
    Ⓖ Many deer lives
    Ⓗ Many deer has lived
    Ⓙ correct as is

❸ <u>**The horses was running**</u> **in the field.**

    Ⓐ The horses were running
    Ⓑ The horses runs
    Ⓒ The horses is running
    Ⓓ correct as is

❹ <u>**The troops has attacked**</u> **the fort.**

    Ⓕ The troops was attacking
    Ⓖ The troops is attacking
    Ⓗ The troops have attacked
    Ⓙ correct as is

Name _____

Fill in the bubble next to the answer that correctly completes each sentence.

1 **Has anyone seen my _____**

Ⓐ jacket.

Ⓑ jacket!

Ⓒ jacket?

Ⓓ jacket"

2 **What a _____**

Ⓕ view?

Ⓖ view!

Ⓗ view.

Ⓙ view;

3 **_____ is our family doctor.**

Ⓐ Dr Martin D. Long

Ⓑ Dr Martin D Long

Ⓒ Dr Martin. D. Long

Ⓓ Dr. Martin D. Long

4 **Abraham Lincoln was born on _____**

Ⓕ February 12, 1809

Ⓖ February 12, 1809.

Ⓗ February, 12 1809.

Ⓙ February, 12, 1809.

Read the poem below. Then answer the questions on the next page. You may look back at this page as you answer the questions.

Albuquerque Turkey

1 Albuquerque is a turkey
2 And he's feathered and he's fine
3 And he wobbles and he gobbles
4 And he's absolutely mine.
5 He's the best pet that you can get.
6 Better than a dog or cat.
7 He's my Albuquerque turkey
8 And I'm awfully proud of that.
9 He once told me, very frankly
10 "I prefer to be your pet,
11 Not the main course at your dinner,"
12 And I told him not to fret.
13 And my Albuquerque turkey
14 Is so happy in his bed,
15 'Cause for our Thanksgiving dinner...
16 We had scrambled eggs instead.

Anonymous

1 Which literary device gives this poem a feeling of fun and lightheartedness?

Ⓐ punctuation

Ⓑ figurative language

Ⓒ rhyme and rhythm

Ⓓ line length

2 Why does the author use quotation marks around the words in lines 10 and 11?

Ⓕ To show what the turkey is saying.

Ⓖ To make the words stand out.

Ⓗ To quote the author.

Ⓙ All poems use quotation marks.

3 In line 15, the ellipsis (...) tell you to _____ before you read line 16.

Ⓐ speed-up

Ⓑ pause

Ⓒ swallow

Ⓓ say, "dot, dot, dot"

4 From which words in the poem do we know that it is told in the first person?

Ⓕ he's, me

Ⓖ mine, my, I'm

Ⓗ bed, dinner

Ⓙ and, in

53

Read the passage below. Then answer the questions on the next page. You may look back at this page as you answer the questions.

Do you think you could jump right on a motorcycle and take off without any instruction or safety gear? Before you try it, here are some things to consider.

First, the cost of the motorcycle does not necessarily include the safety equipment you need to <u>lessen</u> the danger of accidents. If you are riding a used bike, you need to be sure the brakes, brake lights, headlights, horn, and steering mechanism are in good condition.

Next, you need a helmet, even if your state laws do not require one. If you are in an accident and lose an arm, you have another, but how many heads do you have? You may have thought that motorcycle riders wear leather jackets, pants, gloves, and boots just to look tough. That may be true in some cases, but the leather protects their skin in case they fall or are knocked off their <u>bike</u> and skid along the street.

You also need instruction in how to handle this heavy machine safely. You need a driver's license, for which you have to take a test. You should also learn how to "drive defensively." This means that you are always aware of the vehicles around you and what moves they might make. Remember, a motorcycle cannot stop as quickly as a car.

1 The *main* idea of this passage is that motorcycle riders need —

Ⓐ instruction.

Ⓑ safety equipment.

Ⓒ instruction and safety equipment.

Ⓓ helmets.

2 In the third paragraph, <u>bike</u> means —

Ⓕ bicycle.

Ⓖ helmet.

Ⓗ motorcycle.

Ⓙ boots.

3 Why does a motorcycle rider have to take a test?

Ⓐ to get a driver's license

Ⓑ to drive defensively

Ⓒ to wear a helmet

Ⓓ to wear leather clothing

4 The following outline is based on the entire passage. Which point is needed to complete the outline?

I.   Introduction
II. Safety equipment
III. _____
IV. Driving instruction

Ⓕ Helmets   Ⓗ State laws

Ⓖ Protective clothing

55

Name _____

Fill in the bubble next to the word (contraction) that correctly completes each sentence.

1 **Turn in your papers if _____ finished.**

    Ⓐ you're

    Ⓑ your

    Ⓒ your'e

    Ⓓ youa're

2 **I _____ feel well today.**

    Ⓕ dono't

    Ⓖ do'nt

    Ⓗ d'ont

    Ⓙ don't

3 **Mother says _____ going to be late.**

    Ⓐ shees

    Ⓑ she's

    Ⓒ shes'

    Ⓓ s'hes

4 **For dinner tonight, _____ order pizza.**

    Ⓕ well

    Ⓖ we'wll

    Ⓗ we'ill

    Ⓙ we'll

Name _____

To revise your paper you need to review the verbs, nouns, and adjectives. Choose the sentence that would best paint a visual image in the mind of the reader.

1
Ⓐ The book was scary.

Ⓑ The terrifying book gave me goose bumps as I read it.

Ⓒ The scary book made me nervous.

Ⓓ The book was terrifying and scary.

2
Ⓕ The frog hopped to the pond.

Ⓖ The big frog jumped to the pond.

Ⓗ The repulsive frog bounded to the enormous pond.

Ⓙ The frog jumped to the big pond.

3
Ⓐ The steamy spaghetti melted the plastic strainer.

Ⓑ The food was hot.

Ⓒ The food was very hot.

Ⓓ The spaghetti was hot.

4
Ⓕ The cantankerous old man criticized the harried waiter.

Ⓖ The old man criticized the waiter.

Ⓗ The old man complained about the waiter.

Ⓙ The old man criticized the harried waiter.

57

1 **Choose the answer that correctly completes the sentence.**

Charlie _____.

Ⓐ went home
Ⓑ with his two dogs
Ⓒ on his new mountain bike
Ⓓ nervously pacing the floor

2 **Choose the answer that correctly completes the sentence.**

_____ split the tree in two.

Ⓕ With a terrible crack,
Ⓖ During a thunderstorm
Ⓗ Watching from across the valley
Ⓙ A bolt of lightning

3 **Choose the answer that correctly completes the sentence.**

We heard a _____ from the injured man.

Ⓐ grown
Ⓑ groan

4 **Choose the word that tells you *exactly* what Elizabeth saw.**

Elizabeth saw _____ in the sky.

Ⓕ clouds
Ⓖ many clouds
Ⓗ huge, dark thunderclouds
Ⓙ storm clouds

58

Name _____

Read each sentence and look at the underlined words. There may be a mistake in them. Select the best answer to correct the mistake. If there is no mistake, select *correct as is*.

1 They **had given away** all of the kittens by the time we got there.

  Ⓐ have given away
  Ⓑ has given away
  Ⓒ had giving away
  Ⓓ correct as is

2 By 5:00 **Preston will had read** two books.

  Ⓕ Preston will have read
  Ⓖ Preston have read
  Ⓗ Preston will having read
  Ⓙ correct as is

3 By Friday **Caden will have completed** the research part of his report.

  Ⓐ Caden would had completed
  Ⓑ Caden will had completed
  Ⓒ Caden will having completed
  Ⓓ correct as is

4 David **have finished his homework** before school ended.

  Ⓕ have finish his homework
  Ⓖ had finished his homework
  Ⓗ will had finished his homework
  Ⓙ correct as is

59

Name _____

Read each sentence. Choose the word that correctly completes each sentence.

❶ _____ welcome here in our house.

    Ⓐ Your

    Ⓑ You're

❸ "_____ raining!" yelled the students.

    Ⓐ It's

    Ⓑ Its

❷ This is _____ room so you need to clean it.

    Ⓕ your

    Ⓖ you're

❹ The squirrel ate _____ store of nuts during the winter.

    Ⓕ it's

    Ⓖ its

Name _____

Use the dictionary entry to answer the questions below.

club (klub) *n.* **1.** A heavy stick, usually thicker at one end than the other, used as a weapon. **2.** a stick with a crooked head used in golf, hockey, etc. **3.** a group of persons organized for a social, athletic, political, or other purpose. **4.** a black trefoil-shaped figure on a playing card.

❶ Which of the above meanings fits the sentence below?

The caveman used a <u>club</u> to kill animals for food.

Ⓐ Definition **1**

Ⓑ Definition **2**

Ⓒ Definition **3**

Ⓓ Definition **4**

❷ Which of the above meanings fits the sentence below?

The boys invited John to join their <u>club</u>.

Ⓕ Definition **1**

Ⓖ Definition **2**

Ⓗ Definition **3**

Ⓙ Definition **4**

Name _____

Fill in the bubble next to the sentence that explains the <u>underlined words</u> (figure of speech).

❶ **Sarah was <u>having a ball</u> at the school dance. She never wanted it to end.**

Ⓐ Sarah was dancing with a ball.
Ⓑ Sarah was having a great time.
Ⓒ Sarah didn't like the dance.

❷ **I was so frustrated because I couldn't remember the name of Rocki's dog. I just needed another minute to think because it was right <u>on the tip of my tongue</u>.**

Ⓕ The name was written on my tongue.
Ⓖ Rocki was going to tell me the dog's name.
Ⓗ I was almost ready to remember the name.

❸ **Yesterday, Beth and I had an argument. Now she is <u>giving me the cold shoulder</u>.**

Ⓐ Beth is ignoring me.
Ⓑ Beth hurt her shoulder.
Ⓒ Beth is talking to me.

❹ **In Mr. Smith's class you can always <u>hear a pin drop</u>. He is a very strict teacher.**

Ⓕ The students drop pins.
Ⓖ The students are very quiet.
Ⓗ The students do science projects with pins.

62

Name _____

Fill in the bubble next to the word or words that correctly complete each sentence.

1 Jeremy and Robert _____ with Carlita to the movies.

Ⓐ goes

Ⓑ going

Ⓒ went

Ⓓ gone

2 Lois and I _____ the answer to the question.

Ⓕ knowed

Ⓖ has known

Ⓗ knowing

Ⓙ knew

3 Davita, Shiro, and I _____ around the track three times.

Ⓐ have run

Ⓑ have ran

Ⓒ running

Ⓓ runned

4 It is Kyon and Jung's turn to _____ out the trash.

Ⓕ took

Ⓖ taking

Ⓗ taken

Ⓙ take

Read the passage below. Then answer the questions on the next page. You may look back at this page as you answer the questions.

1   A mummy is the body of a person that has been preserved after death. Preservation of a body can happen naturally or by embalming, which is any process that people use to help preserve a dead body. Embalming can occur when a body has been dried out by extreme cold, by the sun, by smoke, or by using chemicals such as natron.

2   Mummification in ancient Egypt was a very long and expensive process. From start to finish, it took about seventy days. There were many steps in the process. First, the body was washed and ritually purified. The next step was to remove the internal organs. After removal of the organs, the body cavity was stuffed with natron. The brain was then removed through the nose using long hooks. Then the body was completely covered with natron and left to dry out for about forty days. The mummy was then prepared for bandaging. The entire body was wrapped with about twenty layers of bandages. Once the mummy was finally prepared, it was time for the funeral.

3   The Pharaohs of ancient Egypt, who were believed to become gods when they died, were mummified and had the most magnificent burials of all. High-ranking officials, priests, and other nobles who had served the Pharaoh and his queen were also mummified. The best-preserved mummies are those of the Pharaohs and their relatives. They were more carefully embalmed and protected from harm.

4   The ancient Egyptians went through this expensive and time-consuming process because they believed that mummifying a person's body after death was essential to ensure a safe passage to the afterlife.

Name _____

1 **Choose the correct four phrases to complete the outline. Write each phrase on the correct line.**

- Mummies around the world

- What is a mummy?

- Mummies today

- Who was mummified?

- The mummification process

- Why mummification?

Egyptian Mummies

I. _____

II. _____

III. _____

IV. _____

Name _____

Fill in the bubble next to the answer that correctly completes each sentence.

1 **To find the locations of cities in the United States, you should look in —**

Ⓐ a dictionary.

Ⓑ a library catalog.

Ⓒ an atlas.

Ⓓ a newspaper.

2 **To find the phone number of a friend, you should look in —**

Ⓕ the telephone directory.

Ⓖ a cookbook.

Ⓗ an encyclopedia.

Ⓙ a dictionary.

3 **To find the titles of books about rockets, you should look in —**

Ⓐ a dictionary.

Ⓑ an encyclopedia.

Ⓒ an atlas.

Ⓓ a library catalog.

4 **To find the meaning of a word, you should look in —**

Ⓕ a science book.

Ⓖ an atlas.

Ⓗ a dictionary.

Ⓙ a magazine.

Name _____

Fill in the bubble next to the answer that correctly completes each sentence.

1 **The teacher chose Demetrio and _____ as captains.**

Ⓐ I
Ⓑ me
Ⓒ she
Ⓓ they

2 **Inez and _____ walked to school together.**

Ⓕ I
Ⓖ me
Ⓗ her
Ⓙ them

3 **She and _____ are identical twins.**

Ⓐ me
Ⓑ her
Ⓒ I
Ⓓ him

4 **The coach got tickets for Mario and _____.**

Ⓕ she
Ⓖ they
Ⓗ he
Ⓙ me

Read the student article, then answer the question.

Keep the victim lying down. If uncertain as to his injuries, keep him flat on his back.

Maintain the victim's normal body temperature. If the weather is cold or damp, place blankets or extra clothing over the victim. If the weather is hot, provide shade.

Get medical assistance as soon as possible. Injury-related shock can be very serious and may even cause death!

1 **Suppose your friend wrote this article. What advice could you give him to improve it?**

Ⓐ Don't indent the paragraphs.

Ⓑ Add an opening sentence that states the topic.

Ⓒ Give the victim's name.

Ⓓ Give more information about the weather.

Name _____

Read each sentence and look at the underlined words. There may be a mistake in them. Select the best answer to correct the mistake. If there is no mistake, select *correct as is*.

❶ I need to move they books from the top shelf to the bottom shelf.

Ⓐ to move this books

Ⓑ to move them books

Ⓒ to move those books

Ⓓ correct as is

❷ George W. Bush, our 43rd President, was born on July 6, 1946.

Ⓕ July, 6, 1946

Ⓖ July 6 1946

Ⓗ ,July 6 1946

Ⓙ correct as is

❸ Sasha was chosed as captain.

Ⓐ was chose as captain

Ⓑ was chosen as captain

Ⓒ was choosed as captain

Ⓓ correct as is

❹ My hat and coat be wet.

Ⓕ hat and coat are wet

Ⓖ hat and coat is wet

Ⓗ hat and coat am wet

Ⓙ correct as is

69

Andrea's teacher asked the students in the class to complete a report. Andrea chose to write about chocolate, her favorite treat. Below is Andrea's first draft. Read the passage and answer the questions on the following page. You may look back at this page as you answer the questions.

---

1   Chocolate has a long history. It <u>comes from</u> the cacao bean, which is grown in many countries near the equator. Over 2,000 years ago it was considered a "food of the gods" by the Mayan Indians.

2   In 1519, Hernando Cortez tasted an Aztec chocolate drink made from the cacao bean. Cortez also saw how the Aztecs treated cacao beans as treasures. He took the beans back to Spain. The bitter taste of the beans was improved when the Spanish heated the drink and added sweeteners. Its formula was kept a secret to be enjoyed by the rich.

Name _____

1 In the second sentence of paragraph 2, which adjective should Andrea add before the word "treasures" to create a better visual image?

Ⓐ old   Ⓒ new
Ⓑ priceless   Ⓓ cheap

---

2 It <u>comes from</u> the cacao bean, which is grown in many countries near the equator.

What is a better way for Andrea to write the underlined part of the sentence?

Ⓕ emanates from   Ⓗ is a product of
Ⓖ springs from   Ⓙ evolves from

3 Which of these sentences could Andrea *best* add at the end of this draft?

Ⓐ Chocolate is still a treasured treat today.
Ⓑ The rich did not want to share with the poor.
Ⓒ The poor eventually stole the formula.

---

4 What is the main idea of this passage?

Ⓕ Chocolate became a treat a long time ago.
Ⓖ Chocolate is the best treat.
Ⓗ Hernando Cortez stole cacao beans from the Aztecs.

71

Name _____

Choose the sentence below that combines all of the numbered sentences in the *best*, most concise way.

 1. **Mother made a cake.**

2. **Mother frosted it with pink icing.**

3. **The cake was for Sarah.**

4. **The cake was for Sarah's birthday.**

Ⓐ Mother made a cake, and mother frosted it with pink icing for Sarah's birthday.

Ⓑ It was Sarah's birthday, and mother made a birthday cake, and it had pink icing.

Ⓒ Sarah's birthday cake, made by her mother, was frosted, and it was with pink icing.

Ⓓ Mother made a cake with pink icing for Sarah's birthday.

 1. **Mark delivers newspapers.**

2. **Mark delivers newspapers every day.**

3. **Mark delivers papers to thirty customers.**

4. **The customers are in Mark's neighborhood.**

Ⓕ Mark has thirty customers in the neighborhood every day Mark delivers newspapers.

Ⓖ Every day Mark delivers newspapers to thirty customers in his neighborhood.

Ⓗ Thirty customers every day in Mark's neighborhood get newspapers delivered by Mark.

Ⓙ Mark delivers thirty customers every day newspapers and they are in the neighborhood.

© BELLWORK Enterprises

Name _____

Fill in the bubble next to the foreign word(s) that correctly complete each sentence.

1 The man was acting like a _____, running around and screaming.

Which Greek word correctly fits into the sentence?

Ⓐ maniac Ⓒ mania

Ⓑ psyche Ⓓ pulley

2 I didn't want to eat a full meal, so I ordered side dishes off the _____ menu.

Which French word/saying correctly fits into the sentence?

Ⓕ au pair Ⓗ au jus

Ⓖ à la carte Ⓙ à la mode

3 Last night my car stopped working; it just went _____.

Which German word correctly fits into the sentence?

Ⓐ kindergarten Ⓒ deli

Ⓑ diesel Ⓓ kaput

4 Lucine's favorite dessert is apple pie _____.

Which French word/saying correctly fits into the sentence?

Ⓕ après-ski Ⓗ art deco

Ⓖ à la carte Ⓙ à la mode

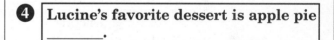

73

Read the passage below. Then answer the questions on the next page. You may look back at this page as you answer the questions.

Tony, who lived in the midwest, was excited about visiting his cousin, Mike, in California. He eagerly looked forward to learning how to windsurf. Before he even unpacked his suitcase, he was asking, "When can we go windsurfing?"

"Not so fast there, <u>Cuz</u>," said Mike. "Before you go windsurfing with me, I've got to make sure you can swim so you don't drown. Then, you have to learn to body surf to get the feel of the waves. After that you can try your luck on a surfboard. That takes some guys all summer!"

"When you finally get on a sailboard," he continued, "you have to keep your balance on a powerful wave while using your feet to keep the board aimed in the direction you want to go. Also, you have to remember everything you know about sailing a boat. Tony, do you know how to sail across the wind and into the wind?"

"But Mike," Tony said dejectedly, "it looks so easy."

1 **In the second paragraph, <u>Cuz</u> is a shortened, slang form of the word —**

Ⓐ California.

Ⓑ suitcase.

Ⓒ cousin.

Ⓓ because.

2 **How do you keep a sailboard aimed in the direction you want to go?**

Ⓕ by using your arms

Ⓖ by using your feet

Ⓗ by using your head

Ⓙ by using your ears

3 **You can tell from this passage that windsurfing —**

Ⓐ is easy to learn.

Ⓑ is not as easy as it looks.

Ⓒ is only for boys.

Ⓓ is only done in California.

4 **To be a good windsurfer, the passage tells us that you should —**

Ⓕ know how to swim.

Ⓖ know how to body surf.

Ⓗ know how to sail a boat.

Ⓙ all of the above

75

Name _____

Fill in the bubble next to the word that comes *second* in alphabetical order.

1

Ⓐ hunch
Ⓑ crunch
Ⓒ bunch
Ⓓ lunch

2

Ⓕ burlap
Ⓖ burly
Ⓗ burn
Ⓙ burlesque

3

Ⓐ rectangle
Ⓑ recreant
Ⓒ recreation
Ⓓ recruit

4

Ⓕ socialism
Ⓖ social
Ⓗ sociology
Ⓙ society

Name _____

Choose the answer that, when added, will form one or more complete sentences.

❶ Ashley read a good _____.

Ⓐ book it was about whales

Ⓑ book. Being about whales

Ⓒ book. It was about whales

Ⓓ book, was about whales

❷ Some seeds are carried by the _____ _____.

Ⓕ wind others hitch rides on animals

Ⓖ wind. Others hitch rides on animals

Ⓗ wind, hitch rides on animals

Ⓙ wind. Hitch rides on animals

❸ I studied hard last _____.

Ⓐ night. I want to do well on the test

Ⓑ night. To do well on the test

Ⓒ night, I want to do well

Ⓓ night. Want to do well on the test

❹ Ona trusted _____.

Ⓕ Sharon. They had been friends for years

Ⓖ Sharon, had been friends for years

Ⓗ Sharon. Having been friends for years

Ⓙ Sharon. Friends for years

77

Read the passage below. Then answer the questions on the next page. You may look back at this page as you answer the questions.

Many times I am asked by my students, "Why do I need to go to college? The job I want does not require a college education." When this question becomes a topic of conversation in the classroom, we have a discussion where I bring up the following three topics:

Most importantly, I stress to them that having a college education will not hurt you. Even if the career you choose doesn't require a college degree, having a degree can only help you. There are many examples of employers choosing a college graduate for a promotion over someone who has not attended college. Even if the degree is not in the area that you are now working in, going to college shows that you can complete a goal that you set for yourself.

Secondly, further into your life you may want to change careers. Many people have changed careers because what interested them when they were twenty years old does not interest them when they are in their forties. Having a college education can make the job change easier.

Finally, a college degree does not have to be a 4-year degree. An Associative Arts (AA) degree, which takes about two years to complete, can also help you advance in the workplace. Employers are looking for people who always want to better themselves and increase their knowledge. Attending a college shows that you want to be a better educated person.

If you don't think that a 4-year university is the best choice for you right now, then attend a community college. If you have to work full-time to support yourself once you graduate from high school, then work during the day and attend classes at night. Earning a college degree gives you options. You will not regret having a college education.

Name _____

1 **Which organizational pattern does the author use in her discussion of a college education?**

Ⓐ comparison and contrast

Ⓑ organization by categories

Ⓒ order of importance

Ⓓ spatial order

---

2 **The author agrees with the concept that having a college education will benefit a person by showing that —**

Ⓕ college is a lot of fun.

Ⓖ having a degree will give a person more options in life.

Ⓗ college is hard.

Ⓙ a community college is a college too.

3 **Which sentence from the passage *best* supports the idea that earning a college degree is better than not attending college?**

Ⓐ Finally, a college degree does not have to be a 4-year degree.

Ⓑ The job I want does not require a college education.

Ⓒ Earning a college degree gives you options.

Ⓓ Having a college education can make the job change easier.

Name _____

❶ The guide words from a dictionary page are:

road — robber

Which word below would be found on this page?

Ⓐ rise   Ⓒ roach

Ⓑ roast   Ⓓ robot

---

❷ The guide words from a dictionary page are:

desperate — detail

Which word below would be found on this page?

Ⓕ despair   Ⓗ detain

Ⓖ detect   Ⓙ dessert

❸ The guide words from a dictionary page are:

sport — spread

Which word below would be found on this page?

Ⓐ spot   Ⓒ spruce

Ⓑ splash   Ⓓ spoon

---

❹ The guide words from a dictionary page are:

flank — flat

Which word below would be found on this page?

Ⓕ flame   Ⓗ flare

Ⓖ flatter   Ⓙ flange

Name _____

❶ Choose the word that is needed for the blank in the letter.

Dear Jason,
  Your mom told me that you have two new ponies on your ranch. She said that they are still somewhat wild and need to be saddle-broken. I hope that _____ will be tame enough by the time I get there in July. I'm looking forward to learning how to ride.

                    Your pal,
                    Robert

Ⓐ she
Ⓑ you
Ⓒ I
Ⓓ they

❷ Choose the word that is needed for the blank in the paragraph.

  Mr. Chung collects clocks from all over the world. He has more than 100 of them. Some are very large and stand on the floor. Others are very small. One is so tiny that it will fit in a teaspoon. His prized possession is an antique cuckoo clock. _____ is very valuable and was made almost 200 years ago.

Ⓕ He
Ⓖ It
Ⓗ They
Ⓙ Them

Read the passage below. Then answer the questions on the next page. You may look back at this page as you answer the questions.

Maria's teacher asked each student to complete a survey of the class and report the findings to her. In the report they needed to also include how this information could be used. Maria decided to survey the class on which types of pencils they preferred to use, regular or mechanical. This is her first draft.

Regular Pencils vs. Mechanical Pencils

After surveying the members of my class, I found that the class was almost split 50/50 in which types of pencils they liked to use.

Fifteen of the students liked to use regular pencils. They liked these types of pencils to write with because they had soft lead that was not too pointy. They also liked the erasers because they lasted a long time. Most of all, they liked that they could get out of their seats and stretch when they needed to sharpen their pencils.

The rest of the students, 17 of them, preferred the mechanical pencils. They liked these pencils because they always had a sharp point and they never had to write with a dull pencil. They thought that the eraser on their pencil lasted just as long as a regular pencil's eraser. The only problem with using this pencil was that the clicking sound in the classroom sometimes frustrated their teacher.

My teacher will be able to use this information to decide what types of pencils to give away during our monthly auctions. Since the class is almost evenly split, she should put the same amount of each pencil in the auction bucket.

82

Name _____

1 **What did a majority of the students think was the same about the pencils?**

Ⓐ the softness of the lead

Ⓑ the sharp point of the pencil

Ⓒ the clicking noise the pencil makes

Ⓓ the eraser

2 **From which words in the selection do we know that it is told in the first person?**

Ⓕ They, she

Ⓖ my, I

Ⓗ teacher, student

Ⓘ their, this

3 **What was different about the two types of pencils?**

Ⓐ The mechanical pencil always has a sharp point while the regular pencil eventually needs sharpening.

Ⓑ The mechanical pencil makes a clicking noise, while the regular pencil does not.

Ⓒ With the regular pencil, a student can get up and stretch when it needs to be sharpened. Mechanical pencils never need to be sharpened.

Ⓓ all of the above

83

❶ Choose the sentence that is the *best* topic sentence (main idea) for the paragraph.

_____ Some people like them fried. You also can poach them by cracking them into gently boiling water, or boil them in their shells. You can beat them and cook them with other ingredients such as cheese and chopped meats or vegetables to make a delicious omelet. You can even drink them in an eggnog.

Ⓐ We usually buy eggs by the dozen.

Ⓑ Eggs should be kept in the refrigerator.

Ⓒ Eggs are eaten in many ways.

Ⓓ White eggs are better than brown eggs.

❷ Choose the sentence for the blank in the paragraph that *best supports* the topic sentence.

Eric Pedranti's seventh-inning double gave the home team a comeback 4-3 victory against the Cincinnati Hawks Thursday night. _____ The drive scored the runner from second base. The victory was especially satisfying for the home team, as they were behind 3-0 in the first inning.

Ⓕ Cincinnati is a large city in southwestern Ohio.

Ⓖ The highest priced ticket for a playoff game is $30.

Ⓗ The championship series is played in October.

Ⓙ The center fielder could only watch as the ball bounced over the fence.

Name _____

Use the sample index to answer the questions.

Reptiles, 29

    Alligators and Crocodiles, 36
    Characteristics of, 30
    Habitats of, 37
    Lizards, 34
    Snakes, 32
    Tortoises (see Turtles)
    Turtles, 35

1 On what page should you look to find information about a king snake?

Ⓐ 32   Ⓒ 37

Ⓑ 36   Ⓓ 29

2 On what page should you look to see if a reptile is warm-blooded?

Ⓕ 36   Ⓗ 37

Ⓖ 34   Ⓙ 30

3 On what page should you look to find information about tortoises?

Ⓐ 36   Ⓒ 37

Ⓑ 35   Ⓓ 32

4 On what page might you look to find where different reptiles live?

Ⓕ 32   Ⓗ 30

Ⓖ 35   Ⓙ 37

Name _____

Fill in the bubble next to the word (plural) that correctly completes each sentence.

1 **Two new _____ were built in the town.**

  Ⓐ factory
  Ⓑ factorys
  Ⓒ factories

2 **Joshua received three new _____.**

  Ⓕ toies
  Ⓖ toys
  Ⓗ toy

3 **Playing with _____ can be dangerous.**

  Ⓐ knife
  Ⓑ knifes
  Ⓒ knives

4 **I felt like I had two left _____.**

  Ⓕ foots
  Ⓖ feet
  Ⓗ feets

Name _____

Read each sentence and look at the underlined words. There may be a mistake in them. Choose the answer to make the sentence correct. If there is no mistake, select *correct as is*.

1 **Birds was building a nest** in the tree in my backyard.

   Ⓐ Birds builded a nest
   Ⓑ Birds have built a nest
   Ⓒ Birds building a nest
   Ⓓ correct as is

2 **The girl's coat** was blue and had a white collar and cuffs.

   Ⓕ The girls coat
   Ⓖ The girls' coat
   Ⓗ The gir'ls coat
   Ⓙ correct as is

3 Our teacher this year is **mrs. thurston.**

   Ⓐ Mrs. Thurston.
   Ⓑ mrs. Thurston.
   Ⓒ Mrs. thurston.
   Ⓓ correct as is

4 Which **rowed** leads to the city?

   Ⓕ road
   Ⓖ rode
   Ⓗ correct as is

87

Read the passage below. Then answer the questions on the next page. You may look back at this page as you answer the questions.

The Lord of the Manor spoke to his woodcutter. "I want a full cord of wood, no more, no less, cut and ready for me when I return in a <u>fortnight</u>."

"Yes, sire, a full cord in a fortnight," agreed the woodcutter.

Now this was an industrious woodcutter, who wasted not a minute. Finishing early on the fourteenth day, he said to his wife, "I think I'll use some of my lord's wood to make a new chair for our table." And he did.

Later that day, his wife saw the lord approaching on horseback.

"Quick, hide the new chair! Put it on the other side of the table," she told the woodcutter. And he did.

Alighting from his horse, the Lord of the Manor entered the woodcutter's cottage to inquire about the good wife's health. Then he went out to collect his wood.

"He didn't mention the new chair," said the wife, "but I'm sure he saw it. Quickly, knock it apart and hide it under the woodpile." And the woodcutter did.

"Didn't I see a new chair at your table, woodcutter?" asked the lord, as he reentered the cottage.

"Oh, no sire. Look again for yourself. It was just your imagination," replied the woodcutter as he watched the lord's servants loading his wood into a horse-drawn cart.

"My, what a big stack of firewood you have," exclaimed the lord.

"Oh, sire, it's just small branches. Too little for you to bother with on your great hearth."

"Mmm, mmm," the lord replied, not quite satisfied.

❶ From the words and language used, you can tell this passage takes place —

Ⓐ in the future.

Ⓑ in the past.

Ⓒ in the present.

Ⓓ yesterday.

❷ How long is a fortnight?

Ⓕ fourteen days

Ⓖ forty days

Ⓗ four days

Ⓙ four weeks

❸ Why did the wife want the chair hidden?

Ⓐ It was not well-made.

Ⓑ It hadn't been painted.

Ⓒ It was made of the lord's wood.

Ⓓ She needed more firewood.

❹ The author probably wrote this passage to —

Ⓕ inform the reader.

Ⓖ argue with issues.

Ⓗ persuade the reader.

Ⓙ entertain the reader.

Name _____

Fill in the bubble next to the answer that correctly completes each sentence.

1 **Newspapers are usually printed —**

Ⓐ on a daily basis.

Ⓑ on a weekly basis.

Ⓒ once a month.

Ⓓ twice a month.

2 **The most important news article of the day usually begins —**

Ⓕ on page 2.

Ⓖ on the front page below the fold.

Ⓗ on the front page above the fold.

Ⓙ the first page of the sports section.

3 **The front page of a newspaper has a _____ that is usually in large font to catch the reader's attention.**

Ⓐ date

Ⓑ headline

Ⓒ picture

Ⓓ mascot

4 **Many newspapers contain a(n) —**

Ⓕ sports section.

Ⓖ business news section.

Ⓗ entertainment section.

Ⓙ all of the above

Name _____

Fill in the bubble next to the answer that correctly completes each sentence.

1 Neil Armstrong was a _____ astronaut.

Ⓐ couragely
Ⓑ courager
Ⓒ courageous
Ⓓ courageness

2 Sean had a bad cold and felt _____.

Ⓕ miserful
Ⓖ miserless
Ⓗ miserness
Ⓙ miserable

3 The tacos were too _____ for me.

Ⓐ spicy
Ⓑ spiceful
Ⓒ spiceable
Ⓓ spiceness

4 A bicycle without wheels is _____.

Ⓕ usely
Ⓖ useness
Ⓗ useless
Ⓙ user

© BELLWORK Enterprises

Name _____

The student who wrote this letter made 5 mistakes in punctuation. Find the 5 mistakes and make the changes.

2-15-05

Julie Perez
1212 Nanche St.
Yourtown IL 61104

Dr. Maria Sanchez
Curator, National History Museum
4140 Bell Road
Anytown, AZ 85201

Dr. Sanchez

I am beginning a report on the burial rites of ancient Egyptians. Please send me any information on your current exhibition of Egyptian mummies Brochures with pictures would be the best. Also please send me a list of books that I could read that would help make my report more interesting.

Thank you

Julie Perez
6th Grade Student

Name _____

1 **What is the difference between <u>reading</u> and <u>comprehending</u>?**

Ⓐ Reading is done for fun; comprehending is hard work.

Ⓑ Reading is done in a book; comprehending is done on T.V.

Ⓒ Reading has to do with stories; comprehending is only listening.

Ⓓ Reading involves recognizing words; comprehending is understanding the words read.

2 **What is the difference between <u>hearing</u> and <u>listening</u>?**

Ⓕ Hearing is recognizing sounds; listening is focusing on the sounds heard and their meaning.

Ⓖ Hearing uses your ears; listening uses your eyes.

Ⓗ Hearing and listening are the same.

Ⓙ none of the above

Name _____

1 **Fill in the bubble next to the sentence that states a *fact*.**

Ⓐ Science is an interesting subject.

Ⓑ Carrots grow under the ground.

Ⓒ Doctors work harder than lawyers.

Ⓓ Chocolate chip cookies are delicious.

2 **Fill in the bubble next to the sentence that states a *fact*.**

Ⓕ Long hair looks better than short hair.

Ⓖ Skiing is more fun than skating.

Ⓗ Washington was our best President.

Ⓙ Lincoln was our 16th President.

3 **Fill in the bubble next to the sentence that states an *opinion*.**

Ⓐ The Earth gets heat from the Sun.

Ⓑ Man has been to the Moon.

Ⓒ Neptune is a planet in our solar system.

Ⓓ Jupiter is more beautiful than Mars.

4 **Fill in the bubble next to the sentence that states an *opinion*.**

Ⓕ Horse stories are interesting.

Ⓖ An encyclopedia contains information.

Ⓗ You can look up words in a dictionary.

Ⓙ Books are found in libraries.

Name _____

Choose the sentence below that combines all of the numbered sentences in the *best*, most concise way.

❶

1. The rain was heavy.
2. The rain fell all night.
3. The rain caused a flood.
4. The flood washed out the bridge.

Ⓐ Rain was heavy, and it fell all night, and it was a flood, and it washed out the bridge.

Ⓑ The bridge was washed out and by a heavy flood that rained all night.

Ⓒ The rain, it was heavy all night, and the rain caused a flood, and it washed out the bridge.

Ⓓ Heavy rain fell all night, causing a flood that washed out the bridge.

❷

1. T. R. Randall is an author.
2. T. R. Randall is my favorite author.
3. T. R. Randall wrote *Wanda's Web*.
4. T. R. Randall wrote *Samuel Little*.

Ⓕ My favorite author, T. R. Randall, wrote *Wanda's Web* and *Samuel Little*.

Ⓖ T. R. Randall wrote *Wanda's Web* and *Samuel Little* and T. R. Randall is my favorite author.

Ⓗ *Wanda's Web* and *Samuel Little* were written by author T. R. Randall and he is my favorite.

Ⓙ T. R. Randall wrote *Wanda's Web* and T. R. Randall wrote *Samuel Little*, my favorite author.

95

Name _____

Read each set of sentences and decide if one of the <u>underlined words</u> is spelled incorrectly, or if there is *no mistake*. Choose your answer and fill in the bubble.

1
Ⓐ Don't <u>lie</u> to your parents.
Ⓑ The dolphin <u>swam</u> under us.
Ⓒ Julio <u>hurryed</u> to catch the bus.
Ⓓ no mistake

2
Ⓕ The <u>croud</u> shouted for their team to win.
Ⓖ Susan saw the accident <u>happen</u>.
Ⓗ We <u>support</u> you in your decision.
Ⓙ no mistake

3
Ⓐ The dog tore the shoes <u>apart</u>.
Ⓑ Have you ever <u>bin</u> to Mexico?
Ⓒ Tran <u>prepared</u> for the game.
Ⓓ no mistake

4
Ⓕ <u>Homework</u> can be fun.
Ⓖ Our <u>sheriff</u> is very nice.
Ⓗ Mrs. Jardine is a pretty <u>wuman</u>.
Ⓙ no mistake

Name _____

Using the encyclopedia pictured below, fill in the bubble next to the correct answer.

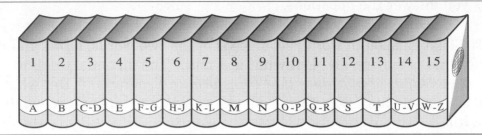

1 **Which volume would you choose to find out about George Washington?**

Ⓐ 5 Ⓒ 11

Ⓑ 9 Ⓓ 15

2 **Which volume would you choose to find information on Susan B. Anthony?**

Ⓕ 1 Ⓗ 12

Ⓖ 2 Ⓙ 13

3 **Which volume would you choose to find information about India?**

Ⓐ 5 Ⓒ 7

Ⓑ 6 Ⓓ 3

4 **In which __two__ volumes might you look to find out about glaciers in Alaska?**

Ⓕ 1 and 10 Ⓗ 2 and 5

Ⓖ 5 and 10 Ⓙ 1 and 5

97

Read the passage below. Then answer the questions on the next page. You may look back at this page as you answer the questions.

Windmill. That compound word is composed of the two words, *wind* and *mill*. You know that the wind is moving air. But what is a mill? The dictionary defines mill as "*any one of various kinds of machines that transform raw material*." But what kind of raw material does a windmill transform? Maybe you didn't think of the wind as raw material, but it is.

You have probably seen pictures of Dutch windmills. They are generally pictured as being built of wood and having four long arms with sails made of cloth. In the United States, windmills have usually been built of steel and have many blades which are joined in the form of a wheel. Wind, striking the angled blades, causes the wheel to turn. The turning wheel makes the machinery work. If the wheel is high enough and not blocked by other structures, it can receive the full force of the wind.

Until recently, most windmills in this country were used to pump water from the ground into storage tanks. But a new type of windmill is springing up in deserts and other windy places. It is being used to generate electricity. These windmills have blades that look like propellers and turn at very high speeds. Near Palm Springs, California, for instance, many acres are being used for these "wind farms."

98

1 **If a windmill were blocked by another structure —**

Ⓐ it would generate electricity.

Ⓑ it might not turn at all.

Ⓒ it would turn backwards.

Ⓓ it would transform raw material.

2 **How might the name, "wind farm," have come to be used?**

Ⓕ Crops are harvested in the wind.

Ⓖ Many farms are located in the desert.

Ⓗ The rows of windmills resemble rows of crops.

Ⓙ Tractors turn the windmills.

3 **In this passage, "springing up" means —**

Ⓐ jumping.

Ⓑ bouncing.

Ⓒ growing.

Ⓓ appearing.

4 **The following outline is based on the entire passage. Which point is needed to complete the outline?**

I. **Meaning of the word, *windmill***

II. **How windmills are made**

III._____

Ⓕ The uses of windmills

Ⓖ How electricity is generated

Ⓗ Palm Springs, California

99

Name _____

Fill in the bubble next to the correct answer.

1 **What does WWW in an Internet address stand for?**

Ⓐ World Wide Ways
Ⓑ Wide Wonderful Website
Ⓒ Website World Ways
Ⓓ World Wide Web

2 **Sammy wants to learn about which ancient civilization buried their dead. Which on-line link would be the best for him to choose?**

Ⓕ U. S. History
Ⓖ Burial Rites
Ⓗ World History
Ⓙ History of Mexico

3 **Carrie wants to e-mail her friend Ned who likes to play the guitar. Which one of the Internet addresses below is an e-mail address?**

Ⓐ www.guitarman.com
Ⓑ http://guitarman.music.com
Ⓒ guitarman@music.com
Ⓓ guitarman.music.com

4 **Kamisha wants to search the on-line encyclopedia for information about the ancient Egyptians and their writing methods. Which on-line link would be best for her to choose?**

Ⓕ Ancient Civilizations
Ⓖ World History
Ⓗ Hieroglyphics
Ⓙ Egypt Today

Name _____

Read the student composition, then answer the question.

_____

_____

   More than seventy-five percent of the world's active volcanoes lie within the "Ring of Fire," a zone which runs along the west coast of the Americas from Alaska to Chile and down the east coast of Asia from Siberia to New Zealand. Twenty percent are located in Indonesia. Others are found in Japan, the Aleutian Islands, Central America, the region around the Mediterranean Sea, and Iceland.

   The world's largest active volcano is Mauna Loa, in Hawaii, which erupted in 1975, and again in 1984.

❶ Suppose you wrote the composition from this outline.

   I.   What is a volcano?
   II. Where volcanoes are located
   III. The largest active volcano

Choose the sentence needed to complete the composition according to the outline.

Ⓐ Vulcan was the Roman god of fire.

Ⓑ A volcano is a vent in the earth's crust from which molten rock and steam erupt.

Ⓒ Volcanic glass is produced by the cooling of molten lava.

Ⓓ The world's largest active volcano is Mauna Loa.

101

Read the passage below. Then answer the questions on the next page. You may look back at this page as you answer the questions.

Last month my brother, Scout, and I went exploring in the mountains. The air was crisp and the ground was covered with powdery snow. We loved running through the snow and collecting it on our coats. Although the snow was chilly, our thick coats protected us. The hair on our paws also protected us from the cold.

That day we decided to follow a trail that had lots of wonderful scents. I headed off, while Scout trotted behind. Hiking was not one of Scout's favorite activities. He actually preferred to sit in front of the fireplace at home. He had a hard time keeping up with me. I had to stop a lot and wait for him. He really needs to get out and run around more. We are twins, but he weighs a lot more than I do because he just doesn't exercise enough.

We were sniffing the trees near us when, all of a sudden, I saw another animal running towards us. Although this animal looked like us, I knew that he was not a friend. As he neared, he began to growl at us. Scout shook with fear. We turned around and began to run back home. Of course, Scout couldn't run fast enough through the snow. As we approached home, I could tell that Scout was not going to make it. The other animal was catching up to him.

I decided that I would have to protect my brother. I started to run towards the other animal. We attacked each other and fell into a huge snowdrift. The snow was very deep, and the other animal became stuck. I managed to get away just as Scout was running into the house. I was sore for the rest of the day, but at least we were both safe.

We decided not to follow the trail by ourselves again. We played close to our house instead and had fun in the snow.

1 This passage is *most* likely —

Ⓐ a narrative written by a student.

Ⓑ a magazine article.

Ⓒ a newspaper article.

Ⓓ an advertisement.

---

2 Scout's brother had to fight the other animal because Scout —

Ⓕ was courageous.

Ⓖ liked the other animal.

Ⓗ was slow and out of shape.

Ⓙ yelled at the other animal.

3 The setting influenced the problem and the resolution —

Ⓐ because the warm sun melted the snow, and Scout ran away.

Ⓑ because the snow slowed Scout down.

Ⓒ because the snow helped Scout's brother.

Ⓓ both Ⓑ and Ⓒ

---

4 The characters in the passage are most likely —

Ⓕ two mice and a rat.

Ⓖ two deer and an elk.

Ⓗ two cats and a tiger.

Ⓙ two dogs and a coyote.

103

Name _____

Use the dictionary entry to answer the questions below.

ring (ring) n. **1**. a circular band of metal or other material, esp. one of gold, for wearing on the finger as an ornament. **2**. a circular line or mark. **3**. a circular course: *to dance in a ring*. **4**. a number of persons or things placed in a circle. **5**. an enclosure in which prize fights take place. **6**. one of the concentric layers of wood produced yearly in the trunks of trees.

❶ Which of the above meanings fits the sentence below?

There was a filthy, black <u>ring</u> in the tub when the children finished bathing the dog.

Ⓐ Definition 1

Ⓑ Definition 2

Ⓒ Definition 4

Ⓓ Definition 6

❷ Which of the above meanings fits the sentence below?

The class formed a large <u>ring</u> to play dodgeball.

Ⓕ Definition 1

Ⓖ Definition 3

Ⓗ Definition 4

Ⓙ Definition 5

104

Name _____

Fill in the bubble next to the word or phrase that correctly completes each statement.

1 **Like a book, magazines also have —**

Ⓐ an index.

Ⓑ a hard cover.

Ⓒ a table of contents.

Ⓓ one author.

2 **Magazines contain —**

Ⓕ one story by one author.

Ⓖ many small articles by different authors.

Ⓗ only advertisements.

Ⓙ writing only with no pictures.

3 **Magazines are published —**

Ⓐ daily.

Ⓑ weekly, biweekly, monthly, or bimonthly.

Ⓒ only once a year.

Ⓓ none of the above

4 **The cover of a magazine —**

Ⓕ lists the publishing date.

Ⓖ only contains the title of the magazine.

Ⓗ never has a picture.

Ⓙ none of the above

❶ Choose the sentence that is the _best_ topic sentence (main idea) for the paragraph.

_____ The crowd in the stadium waited eagerly as the runners took their places. The starter raised his gun and fired the shot that started the race. The runners leaped forward from their starting blocks. The crowd cheered as the runners pounded toward the finish line, with Perez winning by a step!

Ⓐ The big race of the day was about to begin.

Ⓑ The Olympic Summer Games are held every four years.

Ⓒ The stadium seated 60,000 people.

Ⓓ A runner has to train long hours to compete in important track meets.

❷ Choose the sentence for the blank in the paragraph that _best supports_ the topic sentence.

Our pet hamster had escaped from his cage. We discovered he was missing when we got home from school. Jiang had evidently left the door unlatched when she fed him that morning. _____ Then we searched the rest of the house. At last we found him hiding behind the refrigerator.

Ⓕ Since his cage was in our bedroom, we looked there first.

Ⓖ You can buy hamster food at almost any pet store.

Ⓗ Hamsters can be taught to do tricks.

Ⓙ We always make our beds each morning before we go to school.

Name _____

Read each sentence and look at the <u>underlined words</u>. There may be a mistake in them.
Select the best answer to correct the mistake. If there is no mistake, select *correct as is*.

❶ <u>**Four cars finishes**</u> the race.

   Ⓐ Four cars finished
   Ⓑ Four cars was finished
   Ⓒ Four cars is finishing
   Ⓓ correct as is

❷ <u>**Chrysilla have washed her hair**</u>
every day.

   Ⓕ Chrysilla wash her hair
   Ⓖ Chrysilla washing her hair
   Ⓗ Chrysilla washes her hair
   Ⓙ correct as is

❸ The <u>**hot coals burns**</u> the table.

   Ⓐ hot coals was burning
   Ⓑ hot coals is burning
   Ⓒ hot coals were burning
   Ⓓ correct as is

❹ <u>**Several pages missing**</u> **from the**
book.

   Ⓕ Several pages is missing
   Ⓖ Several pages are missing
   Ⓗ Several pages was missing
   Ⓙ correct as is

107

Read the passage below. Then answer the questions on the next page. You may look back at this page as you answer the questions.

Going to camp is a lot of fun. Some schools go to different kinds of camps. A favorite type of camp for many schools is in the mountains. This type of camp is fun because students can hike, learn about nature, and have a great time with their friends. The students also learn about how to take care of nature. Some days the students can do art projects and even help the cook make dinner! Usually at mountain camps there is a night hike one evening. This can be scary, but also a lot of fun. It is exciting to sit quietly and hear all of the different animals that make noises at night. On the other nights it is fun to sit around the campfire and tell stories!

Another type of camp is near the ocean. This type of camp is also a lot of fun. Although some of the experiences are the same, camps near the ocean can offer very different experiences. At ocean camps students make art projects, help the cook with dinner, and sit around the campfire at night. The big difference is in what the students do each day. Instead of hikes, the students at ocean camps get to swim in the ocean each day! The first day they receive a wetsuit that is theirs for the week. They learn how to snorkel and get to see many different types of ocean creatures. Instead of learning about plants and animals in the mountains, they learn about the plants and animals that live in the ocean. They also learn how to keep the ocean safe. The only problem with ocean camp is that you have to be able to swim in order to go with your school!

1 **What activities at both camps are the same?**

Ⓐ art projects, swimming, cooking a meal

Ⓑ art projects, hikes, swimming

Ⓒ campfires, helping to cook a meal, art projects

2 **What activities can students do at ocean camp that they can't do at mountain camp?**

Ⓕ snorkeling, seeing ocean creatures, learning about the ocean and how to keep it safe

Ⓖ art projects, snorkeling, campfires

Ⓗ cooking a meal, hiking, art projects

3 **According to the author, students at ocean camps usually don't go on hikes because —**

Ⓐ there are no trails to follow.

Ⓑ they swim in the ocean each day.

Ⓒ they are too lazy.

4 **Which organizational pattern does the author use in her description of the two types of camps?**

Ⓕ compare and contrast

Ⓖ organizing by categories

Ⓗ order of importance

Read the student essay, then answer the question.

Wind can be both helpful and harmful. For thousands of years, the force of the wind has been used to propel ships across bodies of water. Sailboating and windsurfing are popular sports even today.

Many people harness the force of the wind by using windmills to pump water from deep within the earth.

Large wind machines are used to keep crops from freezing and, more recently, to generate electricity.

The wind is also responsible for carrying seeds of many varieties of plants, thus aiding new growth.

It would seem that wind is more helpful than harmful.

❶ How could you *best* improve this essay?

Ⓐ Begin with a statement that introduces the topic.

Ⓑ End with a statement that sums up all that has been said.

Ⓒ Add at least one example of the harmful effects of the wind.

Ⓓ Tell how windmills pump water.

Name _____

Read each sentence and look at the <u>underlined words</u>. There may be a mistake in them. Select the best answer to correct the mistake. If there is no mistake, select *correct as is*.

❶ <u>**W C. Fields**</u> **was a well-known actor.**

Ⓐ W C Fields
Ⓑ W. C Fields
Ⓒ W. C. Fields
Ⓓ correct as is

❷ **What a great play** <u>**Brett made!**</u>

Ⓕ Brett made"
Ⓖ Brett made?
Ⓗ Brett made;
Ⓙ correct as is

❸ **Wally was born on** <u>**June, 24, 1994.**</u>

Ⓐ June 24 1994.
Ⓑ June 24, 1994.
Ⓒ June, 24 1994.
Ⓓ correct as is

❹ **There were** <u>**almonds, apples and, raisins**</u> **in the cereal.**

Ⓕ almonds, apples, and raisins
Ⓖ almonds apples and raisins
Ⓗ almonds apples, and raisins
Ⓙ correct as is

Read the passage below. Then answer the questions on the next page. You may look back at this page as you answer the questions.

Once upon a time, a miller trapped a baby eagle. He took it home, clipped its wing feathers, and tied it to a post so it couldn't fly.

The baby eagle wanted to regain its freedom. It called and called to its mother and father, but they were too far away to hear. It pecked at its leg bindings, but to no avail. With its shortened wings, it couldn't have flown even if it had gotten free.

By and by, a baker bought the beautiful bird and took it home with him. He fed the eagle, talked to it, and stroked it. He never tied it at all. The bird learned to catch mice and small rabbits and grew bigger and stronger. Finally, its feathers grew long and its wings became strong enough to fly.

One morning it flew a short distance, then came back to the baker. Each day, it flew in ever-widening circles, and then one day it was gone. The baker never expected to see it again. He would miss the magnificent brown bird but was glad that it was free at last.

The next morning, and every morning for a week, the baker found a small rabbit at the door of his shop. "I wonder where those rabbits are coming from?" he thought.

1 **From this passage, you can tell that if you clip a bird's wing feathers —**

Ⓐ it cannot eat.

Ⓑ it cannot call.

Ⓒ it cannot stand.

Ⓓ it cannot fly.

2 **The miller in this passage can *best* be described as —**

Ⓕ cruel and selfish.

Ⓖ rich and famous.

Ⓗ wise and thoughtful.

Ⓙ a nature lover.

3 **At the end of the passage, where did the rabbits come from?**

Ⓐ The miller brought them.

Ⓑ A mother rabbit left them.

Ⓒ They hopped there by themselves.

Ⓓ The eagle brought them to show his thanks.

4 **What is the *best* theme for this passage?**

Ⓕ "A bird in the hand is worth two in the bush."

Ⓖ "Don't count your chickens before they hatch."

Ⓗ "Freedom is a cherished possession."

Ⓙ "Smile, and the world smiles with you."

113

Read the poem below. Then answer the questions that follow.

"Swat!"

Buzz went the fly.

Splat went the moth.

Zap went the mosquito

Stung by the shock.

Aiming for the insects.

Be careful...1,2,3.

Watch out for the fly swatter

It stings like a bee.

❶ The first stanza of this poem uses —

Ⓐ alliteration.

Ⓑ onomatopoeia.

Ⓒ consonance.

Ⓓ assonance.

❷ Who is the author of this poem?

Ⓕ Swat!

Ⓖ a mosquito

Ⓗ a bee

Ⓙ an anonymous author

Students learn at school through different **modalities**. **Aural** learners are the most common; they learn best by listening. Visual learners learn best by seeing information in print. Other students learn best through hands-on activities.

① **From this passage you can tell that modalities probably —**

Ⓐ has to do with the senses.

Ⓑ means having your picture taken.

Ⓒ are small versions of cars that you put together.

Ⓓ means to move around.

② **From this paragraph you can tell that aural probably means —**

Ⓕ sight.

Ⓖ oral.

Ⓗ tactile.

Ⓙ hearing.

③ **Which sentence best helps you understand the meaning of aural?**

Ⓐ Other students learn best through hands-on activities.

Ⓑ They learn best by listening.

Ⓒ Visual learners learn best by seeing information in print.

Ⓓ Students learn at school through different modalities.

115

Name _____

Fill in the bubble next to the answer that correctly completes each sentence.

❶ The movie, _____, was very funny.

   Ⓐ Home Now
   Ⓑ home Now
   Ⓒ Home now
   Ⓓ home now

❷ The children rode their bikes to _____.

   Ⓕ hillcrest park
   Ⓖ Hillcrest park
   Ⓗ hillcrest Park
   Ⓙ Hillcrest Park

❸ Natasha was born in _____, Texas.

   Ⓐ san Antonio
   Ⓑ San antonio
   Ⓒ San Antonio
   Ⓓ san antonio

❹ The _____ is in Washington, D.C.

   Ⓕ Lincoln Memorial
   Ⓖ lincoln memorial
   Ⓗ Lincoln memorial
   Ⓙ lincoln Memorial

Name _____

1 **Choose the word that comes *third* in alphabetical order.**

Ⓐ bit

Ⓑ bite

Ⓒ bitter

Ⓓ blackmail

---

2 **Which dictionary guide words would be on the page where you would find the word *easy*?**

Ⓙ each — east

Ⓚ Easter — eddy

Ⓔ eat — edge

Ⓟ edict — effusion

3 **Choose the sentence that states an *opinion*.**

Ⓐ Mexico lies south of the United States.

Ⓑ The population of Mexico is over 100 million.

Ⓒ Mexico City is the capital of Mexico.

Ⓓ Mexico City is Mexico's most beautiful city.

---

4 **Choose the word that tells you what Emily *heard*.**

Emily heard bees _____ in the flowers.

Ⓙ flying   Ⓔ landing

Ⓚ moving   Ⓟ buzzing

1 **I had always trusted her until she lied to me.**

The verb tense in this sentence is —

Ⓐ past perfect.
Ⓑ present perfect.
Ⓒ future perfect.
Ⓓ none of the above

2 **Stephanie will have finished the book before you even start it.**

The verb tense in this sentence is —

Ⓕ past perfect.
Ⓖ present perfect.
Ⓗ future perfect.
Ⓙ none of the above

3 **Has anyone seen my math homework?**

The verb tense in this sentence is —

Ⓐ past perfect.
Ⓑ present perfect.
Ⓒ future perfect.
Ⓓ none of the above

4 **I have already finished all of my chores.**

The verb tense in this sentence is —

Ⓕ past perfect.
Ⓖ present perfect.
Ⓗ future perfect.
Ⓙ none of the above

Name _____

For each item below, choose the word that means the *same or almost the same* (synonym) as the <u>underlined word</u>.

1 the <u>rear</u> seat

Ⓐ right
Ⓑ ready
Ⓒ soft
Ⓓ back

2 be in a <u>hurry</u>

Ⓕ puzzle
Ⓖ rush
Ⓗ mystery
Ⓙ discomfort

3 a <u>major</u> decision

Ⓐ small
Ⓑ good
Ⓒ important
Ⓓ sensible

4 a <u>portion</u>

Ⓕ large
Ⓖ total
Ⓗ several
Ⓙ part

119

Name _____

Choose the sentence below that combines all of the numbered sentences in the *best,* most concise way.

❶
1. **The kilt is a pleated skirt.**
2. **The kilt is knee-length.**
3. **It is worn by men.**
4. **It is worn in Scotland.**

Ⓐ The kilt is a pleated skirt, and it is worn by men, it is knee-length, in Scotland.

Ⓑ The kilt is a pleated skirt, and it is knee-length, worn by men in Scotland.

Ⓒ The kilt is a pleated skirt, worn by knee-length men in Scotland.

Ⓓ The kilt is a knee-length, pleated skirt worn by men in Scotland.

❷
1. **Garlic is an herb.**
2. **Garlic belongs to the lily family.**
3. **Garlic is widely-grown.**
4. **It is used in cooking.**

Ⓕ Garlic is an herb, and it is in the lily family, and it is widely grown for cooking.

Ⓖ Garlic, an herb, of the lily family, widely-grown, and it is used in cooking.

Ⓗ Herb, a garlic of the lily family, is widely-cooked.

Ⓙ Garlic is a widely-grown herb of the lily family that is used in cooking.

Name _____

Read each sentence and look at the underlined words. There may be a mistake in them. Select the best answer to correct the mistake. If there is no mistake, select *correct as is*.

❶ **Julie isnt going** to school today.

    Ⓐ Julie is'nt going
    Ⓑ Julie i'snt going
    Ⓒ Julie isn't going
    Ⓓ correct as is

❷ When I get home, **Ill' watch TV**.

    Ⓕ Ill watch TV
    Ⓖ I'll watch TV
    Ⓗ Il'l watch TV
    Ⓙ correct as is

❸ **They'are all going** to Don's birthday party.

    Ⓐ The'yre all going
    Ⓑ They're all going
    Ⓒ Theyr'e all going
    Ⓓ correct as is

❹ **It's a beautiful day** today!

    Ⓕ Itis a beautiful day
    Ⓖ Its' a beautiful day
    Ⓗ Its a beautiful day
    Ⓙ correct as is

Read the passage below. Then answer the questions on the next page. You may look back at this page as you answer the questions.

Do you read the comic section of the newspaper? If so, you know it consists of comic strips and cartoons. Do you know the history of comic strips and cartoons?

Actually, the word cartoon comes from the Italian word "cartone," meaning a large sheet of paper. In 1515 and 1516 the artist Raphael used sheets of paper approximately 10 or 11 feet high and 13 to 17 feet wide on which to make drawings and paintings as designs for tapestries. These tapestries were to be woven and hung in the Sistine Chapel of the Vatican in Rome. It is an awesome experience to stand before these magnificent paintings that now hang in the Victoria and Albert Museum in London. The viewer seems to be a part of the life-sized scene.

Not many years ago, a famous studio in California invented a way of making the characters in still pictures appear to move. This is called <u>animation</u>, and it led to the cartoons children now watch on TV and some full-length adventure movies.

As you can see, comic strips and cartoons have been around for centuries. Their evolution has changed over the years, but the idea has stayed the same.

Name _____

① **The word *cartoon* comes from —**

    Ⓐ an Italian word.

    Ⓑ the artist, Raphael.

    Ⓒ California.

    Ⓓ the Vatican in Rome.

② **You can tell from this passage that —**

    Ⓕ a studio in California created cartoons.

    Ⓖ the artist Raphael made miniature drawings and paintings.

    Ⓗ cartoons have been around for several hundred years.

    Ⓙ the Sistine Chapel is in London.

③ **In the process of <u>animation</u>, —**

    Ⓐ characters are big.

    Ⓑ characters are life-sized.

    Ⓒ characters are mysterious.

    Ⓓ characters appear to move.

④ **The large paintings of Raphael that the passage describes, now hang in —**

    Ⓕ the Sistine Chapel.

    Ⓖ London's Victoria and Albert Museum.

    Ⓗ a studio in California.

    Ⓙ a comic strip.

123

Read the passage below. Then answer the questions on the next page. You may look back at this page as you answer the questions.

It was the middle of the night when Avani woke up and jumped out of bed. The ceiling fan was swaying - it was an earthquake! Avani didn't know where to go. She was visiting her aunt and uncle and didn't know the layout of their house very well. The bed was shaking so hard that it began to move across the hardwood floor. Avani was afraid that the ceiling fan would fall on her. The bookshelf also started to sway away from the wall! She began to scream and cry. Suddenly her door flew open, and there stood her aunt.

"Hurry! We need to get under the dining room table!" her aunt screamed.

Avani ran behind her aunt and hid under the table. Her aunt and uncle were very calm and tried to reassure the crying Avani.

After the earthquake ended, Avani's uncle explained that he had made the table by hand. It was so sturdy that during an earthquake, it was the safest place to hide.

When the earthquake was over, Avani thanked her aunt and uncle for taking care of her.

1 You can tell that this passage is realistic fiction because it —

Ⓐ has a happy ending.

Ⓑ has characters talking.

Ⓒ is a myth passed down from generation to generation.

Ⓓ is a story that could happen.

2 Which sentence *best* states the theme of the passage?

Ⓕ Earthquakes can cause damages.

Ⓖ People can react to dangerous situations in different ways.

Ⓗ Don't stand under a ceiling fan during an earthquake.

Ⓙ Big tables are better than small tables.

3 Which sentence *best* supports the theme of the passage?

Ⓐ The bookshelf also started to sway from the wall!

Ⓑ Her aunt and uncle were very calm and tried to reassure the crying Avani.

Ⓒ Avani was afraid that the ceiling fan would fall on her.

Ⓓ During an earthquake, under the table was the safest place to hide.

4 This passage is written from which point of view?

Ⓕ first person

Ⓖ third person

125

Name _____

Use this table of contents from a cookbook to answer the questions below.

Table of Contents

	Page
The Appetizer Table.	1
The Soup Pot	8
The Salad Bar	19
The Main Dish Medley	35
The Bakery Shop	57
The Vegetable Stand	95
The Dairy Bar	105

1 If you wanted to find out how to prepare and cook fresh peas, you should probably look in the section that begins on page —

Ⓐ 8.

Ⓑ 19.

Ⓒ 95.

Ⓓ 105.

2 If you are preparing a recipe that is on page 40 in this book, you are making —

Ⓕ an appetizer.

Ⓖ a salad.

Ⓗ a main dish.

Ⓙ a dessert.

Name _____

Fill in the bubble next to the word (plural) that correctly completes each sentence.

1 **There are several _____ in February.**

   Ⓐ holiday

   Ⓑ holidays

   Ⓒ holidaies

2 **My hamburger has two meat —**

   Ⓕ patty.

   Ⓖ pattys.

   Ⓗ patties.

3 **Susan helped her father rake —**

   Ⓐ leaf.

   Ⓑ leafs.

   Ⓒ leaves.

4 **In Yellowstone, we saw many —**

   Ⓕ deer.

   Ⓖ deers.

   Ⓗ deeres.

127

Name _____

Read each sentence and look at the underlined words. There may be a mistake in them. Select the best answer to correct the mistake. If there is no mistake, select *correct as is*.

1 <u>I have written a letter</u> to my grandfather.

    Ⓐ I writed a letter
    Ⓑ I writing a letter
    Ⓒ I have wrote a letter
    Ⓓ correct as is

2 <u>We seen the fireworks</u> show at the park.

    Ⓕ We had saw the fireworks
    Ⓖ We saw the fireworks
    Ⓗ We seed the fireworks
    Ⓙ correct as is

3 <u>Father fell from the ladder</u> and hurt his arm.

    Ⓐ Father fall from the ladder
    Ⓑ Father falling from the ladder
    Ⓒ Father fallen from the ladder
    Ⓓ correct as is

4 <u>The bell has rang</u>; recess is over.

    Ⓕ The bell ringed
    Ⓖ The bell rung
    Ⓗ The bell has rung
    Ⓙ correct as is

Name _____

Fill in the bubble next to the word (pronoun) that correctly completes each sentence.

① **A guard met _____ at the gate.**

Ⓐ he
Ⓑ him
Ⓒ she
Ⓓ they

② **The bus stopped for Tony and _____.**

Ⓕ I
Ⓖ me
Ⓗ he
Ⓙ they

③ **Alexis bought _____ for her brother.**

Ⓐ they
Ⓑ them
Ⓒ their
Ⓓ we

④ **The puppy followed Kelly and _____.**

Ⓕ we
Ⓖ they
Ⓗ he
Ⓙ me

Olivia's teacher asked each student to research an aspect of Pilgrim life. Olivia used a CD-ROM encyclopedia. Look at the encyclopedia below, then answer the questions on the next page.

A MIDDLETON ENCYCLOPEDIA COLLECTION

Pilgrims

Click on the topic you would like to search.

➤ Daily Life   ➤ Transportation
➤ Clothing   ➤ Religion
➤ Food   ➤ Work Life
➤ Homes   ➤ Family History

SEARCH: [_____] **GO**

Name _____

You may look back at the CD-ROM as you answer the questions below.

1 **Which encyclopedia collection is this CD-ROM made from?**

Ⓐ Pilgrims

Ⓑ Middleton

Ⓒ CD-ROM

Ⓓ Research

2 **To find information on one of the listed topics, what should Olivia do?**

Ⓕ click on the GO button

Ⓖ click on the topic

Ⓗ highlight the topic

Ⓙ click once on SEARCH

3 **What does Olivia's teacher want her to do?**

Ⓐ research encyclopedias

Ⓑ research CD-ROMs

Ⓒ write a paper about computers

Ⓓ research Pilgrim life

4 **If Olivia wants to learn more about what Pilgrims wore, what should she do?**

Ⓕ click on the GO button

Ⓖ highlight Family History

Ⓗ click on Clothing

Ⓙ click once on Work Life

131

Use this section of a map to answer the questions.

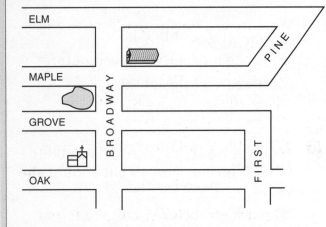

School
Church
Park

N
W ✦ E
S

1 The longest street running north and south is —

Ⓐ Elm.　　Ⓒ First.

Ⓑ Broadway.　Ⓓ Pine.

2 A park lies directly between —

Ⓕ Elm and Maple.　Ⓗ Maple and Pine.

Ⓖ Grove and Oak.　Ⓙ Maple and Grove.

3 What is on the northeast corner of Broadway and Maple?

Ⓐ a church　Ⓒ a park

Ⓑ a school　Ⓓ nothing

4 How many blocks north of Oak is Elm?

Ⓕ 1　　Ⓗ 3

Ⓖ 2　　Ⓙ 4

Name _____

1 The guide words from a dictionary page are:

ideal — idiom

Which word below would be found on this page?

Ⓐ icicle   Ⓒ idol

Ⓑ ignorant   Ⓓ identity

---

2 The guide words from a dictionary page are:

minor — miracle

Which word below would be found on this page?

Ⓕ mint   Ⓗ mirage

Ⓖ mine   Ⓙ mischief

3 The guide words from a dictionary page are:

sitter — skeletal

Which word below would be found on this page?

Ⓐ sister   Ⓒ size

Ⓑ skull   Ⓓ skit

---

4 The guide words from a dictionary page are:

pastel — patent

Which word below would be found on this page?

Ⓕ paste   Ⓗ pattern

Ⓖ patent   Ⓙ paint

133

Name _____

Learn Tae Kwon Do Now!

Take Tae Kwon Do lessons to:

- BUILD YOUR STRENGTH!
- DEVELOP YOUR CONCENTRATION!
- EXERCISE!

Three months of training and you'll be able to defend yourself against anyone!

1 **Which phrase from the ad is most likely <u>not</u> true?**

Ⓐ Build your strength!

Ⓑ Three months of training and you'll be able to defend yourself against anyone!

Ⓒ Develop your concentration!

Ⓓ Exercise!

2 **You want to change the artwork on this ad. When searching for new clip art on your computer, what would be the *best* keyword to use in the "search" box?**

Ⓕ kicking

Ⓖ jumping

Ⓗ tae kwon do

Ⓙ defense

Name _____

❶ | **The cat meowed, and the fire crackled.**

The writing technique that uses words that sound like what they are is called _____.

Ⓐ metaphor   Ⓒ assonance

Ⓑ simile   Ⓓ onomatopoeia

---

❷ | **The June gloom loomed over the flute player.**

The writing technique that uses repeated vowel sounds is called _____.

Ⓕ metaphor   Ⓗ assonance

Ⓖ simile   Ⓙ onomatopoeia

❸ | **The bug was as big as an apple.**

The writing technique that compares two things using "like" or "as" is called _____.

Ⓐ metaphor   Ⓒ assonance

Ⓑ simile   Ⓓ onomatopoeia

---

❹ | **My little sister is a monster.**

The writing technique that compares two things by saying one is the other is called _____.

Ⓕ metaphor   Ⓗ assonance

Ⓖ simile   Ⓙ onomatopoeia

135

Read the passage below. Then answer the questions on the next page. You may look back at this page as you answer the questions.

An *almanac* is a book or pamphlet containing various kinds of information and is usually published once a year. Historians believe there were almanacs in the ancient Roman Empire. The older almanacs included a calendar with times of the rising and setting sun, the phases of the moon, weather predictions, and other information useful to farmers.

In England, the *Nautical Almanac*, one of several published in the 1600's, was written for sailors.

One of the best known almanacs in this country was *Poor Richard's Almanac*. It was written by Benjamin Franklin and first published for the year 1733. In it was information on the courts and the roads, as well as poems and <u>proverbs</u>. Many of these short sayings are still quoted today.

The *World Almanac* has been published each year since 1868 and contains general information. It is almost like a "mini-encyclopedia." Many organizations and groups also publish almanacs containing information of special interest to their members.

1 **You can tell from this passage that a <u>proverb</u> is —**

Ⓐ a poem.

Ⓑ a mini-encyclopedia.

Ⓒ a short saying.

Ⓓ a calendar.

2 **Benjamin Franklin wrote —**

Ⓕ The *Nautical Almanac*.

Ⓖ the *World Almanac*.

Ⓗ *Poor Richard's Almanac*.

Ⓙ an ancient Roman almanac.

3 **Which of the almanacs mentioned is still being published yearly?**

Ⓐ the *Nautical Almanac*

Ⓑ the *World Almanac*

Ⓒ *Poor Richard's Almanac*

Ⓓ an ancient Roman almanac

4 **An almanac can best be compared to —**

Ⓕ a dictionary.

Ⓖ an atlas.

Ⓗ a telephone directory.

Ⓙ an encyclopedia.

Name _____

Read each sentence and look at the underlined words. There may be a mistake in them. Select the best answer to correct the mistake. If there is no mistake, select *correct as is*.

---

1 Are there <u>fish in this lake</u>?

  Ⓐ fish in them lake
  Ⓑ fish in these lake
  Ⓒ fish in those lake
  Ⓓ correct as is

---

2 Please put the <u>books on them shelf</u>.

  Ⓕ books on this shelf
  Ⓖ books on this here shelf
  Ⓗ books on these shelf
  Ⓙ correct as is

---

3 <u>Those man in the blue coat</u> is my father.

  Ⓐ That man in the blue coat
  Ⓑ Them man in the blue coat
  Ⓒ These man in the blue coat
  Ⓓ correct as is

---

4 All <u>them apples</u> are ripe.

  Ⓕ those there apples
  Ⓖ these here apples
  Ⓗ those apples
  Ⓙ correct as is

Name _____

❶ Choose the sentence that is the *best* topic sentence (main idea) for the paragraph.

_____ They begin as tiny eggs from which the larvae hatch. The larvae eat mulberry leaves and grow very rapidly. When they are about as long as your index finger, they spin a cocoon of silk. Inside the cocoon, metamorphosis takes place, and the silkworm emerges as a moth.

Ⓐ Silk is an expensive fabric that comes in many colors.

Ⓑ Silkworms have a very interesting life cycle.

Ⓒ Butterflies and moths are similar, but have unique characteristics.

Ⓓ Most moths are night-flying insects that are attracted to light.

❷ Choose the sentence for the blank in the paragraph that *best supports* the topic sentence.

The largest body of fresh water in the world is formed by the Great Lakes. Five lakes make up the Great Lakes: Lake Erie, Lake Huron, Lake Michigan, Lake Ontario, and Lake Superior. _____ _____ The other four are shared with Canada.

Ⓕ Lake Tahoe is a beautiful lake on the California/Nevada border.

Ⓖ A lake is a body of water surrounded by land.

Ⓗ Canada is a large country lying north of the United States.

Ⓙ Lake Michigan is the only one of the Great Lakes entirely within the United States.

139

The British and American governments are <u>allies</u>. They support each other in times of crises. The two governments have similar <u>dispositions</u> when it comes to world relations.

❶ From this paragraph you can tell that <u>allies</u> probably means —

Ⓐ a narrow street.

Ⓑ they are enemies.

Ⓒ two or more groups that support each other.

Ⓓ they dislike one another.

❷ From this paragraph you can tell that <u>dispositions</u> probably means —

Ⓕ attitudes.

Ⓖ a formal written document.

Ⓗ anger.

Ⓙ temperature.

❸ Which sentence *best* helps you understand the meaning of <u>allies</u>?

Ⓐ The two governments have similar dispositions when it comes to world affairs.

Ⓑ They support each other in times of crises.

Ⓒ The British and American governments are allies.

Ⓓ none of the above

Name _____

Read each sentence. Fill in the bubble next to the correct answer (indefinite pronoun).

1 **I want one of _____ candy.**

Ⓐ all

Ⓑ any

Ⓒ every

Ⓓ none

3 **_____ day is fine for me!**

Ⓐ Many

Ⓑ None

Ⓒ Any

Ⓓ Few

2 **Our dog wouldn't eat _____ of his food.**

Ⓕ any

Ⓖ every

Ⓗ none

Ⓙ each

4 **_____ of us got to hit the ball.**

Ⓕ Every

Ⓖ Other

Ⓗ No

Ⓙ Each

Name _____

Using the encyclopedia pictured below, fill in the bubble next to the correct answer.

1 Which volume would you choose to find out about Dwight D. Eisenhower?

Ⓐ 4   Ⓒ 11

Ⓑ 3   Ⓓ 6

2 Which volume would be best to find information on the island of Puerto Rico?

Ⓕ 6   Ⓗ 11

Ⓖ 10   Ⓙ 12

3 Which volume would you choose to find information about Brigham Young?

Ⓐ 2   Ⓒ 12

Ⓑ 6   Ⓓ 15

4 In which <u>two</u> volumes might you look to find out about volcanoes in Hawaii?

Ⓕ 6 and 13   Ⓗ 14 and 15

Ⓖ 6 and 14   Ⓙ 9 and 15

Name _____

Choose the sentence below that combines all of the numbered sentences in the *best*, most concise way.

❶
1. **Tuna live in the ocean.**
2. **Halibut live in the ocean.**
3. **Trout live in fresh water.**
4. **Catfish live in fresh water.**

Ⓐ Tuna and halibut live in the ocean, but trout and catfish live in fresh water.

Ⓑ Tuna live in the ocean, halibut live in the ocean, trout live in fresh water, catfish live in fresh water.

Ⓒ Tuna live in the ocean, and halibut live in the ocean, and trout live in fresh water, and catfish live in fresh water.

❷
1. **A tornado occurred in Kansas.**
2. **A tornado occurred in Iowa.**
3. **An earthquake occurred in California.**
4. **An earthquake occurred in Alaska.**

Ⓕ Tornadoes occurred in Kansas and Iowa, while earthquakes occurred in California and Alaska.

Ⓖ Tornadoes occurred in Kansas and Iowa, an earthquake occurred in California, and an earthquake occurred in Alaska.

Ⓗ A tornado occurred in Kansas, a tornado occurred in Iowa, an earthquake occurred in California, an earthquake occurred in Alaska.

Look at the website page below. Then answer the questions on the following page. You may look back at this page as you answer the questions.

YOUR ACCOUNT   STORE LOCATOR   SHOPPING BAG

STEP INTO SPRING
with Marston's

New **Spring Shoe Fashions**

Save up to 25% if
you place your order
before April 2nd

SALE   SALE   SALE   SALE   SALE

women's
• dresses
• pants
• shoes

men's
• pants
• shorts
• shirts
• shoes

Spring Sale Items

Swimsuit Collection

browse everything:
men's, women's, children's

144

1 **What is this website advertising?**

Ⓐ surfboards

Ⓑ warm weather

Ⓒ summer activities

Ⓓ spring fashions

2 **What persuasive strategies does this website use to get you to buy their merchandise?**

Ⓕ testimonials

Ⓖ peer pressure

Ⓗ bright colors

Ⓙ repetition

3 **How can you save up to 25%?**

Ⓐ order at least two items

Ⓑ place your order before April 2nd

Ⓒ browse women's, men's, and children's

Ⓓ place your order after April 2nd

4 **Which of the following is not something Marston's carries in women's clothing?**

Ⓕ dresses

Ⓖ shorts

Ⓗ shoes

Ⓙ pants

Name _____

The student who wrote this letter made 5 mistakes in capitalization *and* punctuation.
Find the 5 mistakes and make the changes.

 1

1-15-04

Connie Lu
1111 Elk grove St.
Mytown, WA 99163

Gustavo Lopez
School Services, Inc.
1443 sacramento St.
Anytown, CA 93106

Dear Mr. Lopez

I am writing on behalf of my class. We recently saw an advertisement for
your cardboard pencil boxes. However, we could not find any ordering
information. Please send us an order form. Although you advertise them as
pencil boxes we plan to use them for many different projects.

Thank you

Connie Lu

Name _____

Liam's teacher asked the class to learn about a discovery that has changed their lives and write about what they learned. Liam wants to write about the discovery of rubber.

❶ To complete this assignment, Liam will write a _____.

Ⓐ letter to the editor
Ⓑ poem
Ⓒ personal narrative
Ⓓ factual report

❷ Liam wants to search his encyclopedia on CD-ROM for information on his topic. Which set of words would be the *best* to use to begin the search using the CD's search function?

Ⓕ rubber, history of
Ⓖ rubber bands
Ⓗ tires
Ⓙ balls, erasers, etc.

❸ If Liam wants each of his paragraphs to be indented, which word processing function should be used?

Ⓐ margins
Ⓑ spell-check
Ⓒ caps lock
Ⓓ first line indent

❹

> Rubber has many uses.
> *Car tires are made of rubber.*

The two sentences above are written in different _____.

Ⓕ screens   Ⓗ fonts
Ⓖ tools   Ⓙ computers

Read the passage below. Then answer the questions on the next page. You may look back at this page as you answer the questions.

When Paul awoke one morning, he had a headache and a backache. He also felt hot. When he tried to get up, his legs wouldn't work. Soon his neck, legs, and back hurt much worse. Hospital tests proved what everyone had feared. Like hundreds of other children in the 1940's, Paul had polio!

Doctors said he had to rest in bed until the fever went down. Nurses put very warm, wet towels on his aching back and paralyzed legs. Then his stiff muscles had to be stretched and exercised. After months of painful practice, he learned to walk again. But he would always have to use crutches and leg braces.

Paul always wondered why he was the only one in his family to get polio. He read all he could find about the disease and eventually went on to become a doctor. He hoped to help other people keep their bodies healthy and strong in order to avoid getting diseases like polio.

After years of research by many people, a medical breakthrough took place in 1953. An American physician by the name of Jonas Salk had perfected a vaccine for polio! This vaccine was administered as a shot. Then, two years later, another American, Albert Sabin, perfected a polio vaccine that could be taken by mouth instead of as a shot. People all over the world rejoiced that the spread of the crippling disease could at last be controlled.

1 Will you please <u>sign</u> my yearbook? In this question, the word sign means —

Ⓐ the language used by the hearing impaired.

Ⓑ a hint.

Ⓒ to autograph (*the action word*).

---

2 I lost my <u>watch</u>. In this sentence watch means —

Ⓕ to guard.

Ⓖ to look at (*the action word*).

Ⓗ a timepiece.

3 Sarah went to a <u>show</u> with her friend. In this sentence, show means —

Ⓐ a performance.

Ⓑ to display (*the action word*).

Ⓒ to illustrate (*the action word*).

---

4 What <u>kind</u> of ice cream do you want? In this question, kind means —

Ⓕ caring.

Ⓖ gentle.

Ⓗ a type or variety.

Name _____

1 Which of the following is *not* mentioned in the passage as a symptom of polio?

Ⓐ an upset stomach

Ⓑ a headache

Ⓒ a backache

Ⓓ paralyzed legs

2 Which of the following treatments was used for Paul's aching back?

Ⓕ bed rest

Ⓖ stretching

Ⓗ exercising

Ⓙ warm, wet towels

3 The Sabin oral vaccine became available in —

Ⓐ the 1940's.

Ⓑ 1953.

Ⓒ 1954.

Ⓓ 1955.

4 You can tell from this passage that vaccines are used to —

Ⓕ cure a disease.

Ⓖ control the spread of a disease.

Ⓗ reduce a fever.

Ⓙ cure paralyzed legs.

149

Name _____

Read each set of sentences and decide if one of the underlined words is spelled incorrectly, or if there is *no mistake*. Choose your answer and fill in the bubble.

1

Ⓐ Maria checked out a book from the liberry.

Ⓑ He took aim at the target.

Ⓒ The earthquake shook the house.

Ⓓ no mistake

2

Ⓕ The carnival is this Saturday.

Ⓖ A merry-go-round is circular.

Ⓗ Greg deosn't have a ticket to the game.

Ⓙ no mistake

3

Ⓐ Fall is a pretty season in Utah.

Ⓑ Mother bought fresh fruit at the market.

Ⓒ The movie bored us to tears.

Ⓓ no mistake

4

Ⓕ He placed doubt in their minds.

Ⓖ Some lamps are made of brass.

Ⓗ The president gave an important speach.

Ⓙ no mistake

Read the poem below. Then answer the questions on the next page. You may look back at this page as you answer the questions.

"Your Love"

1 Your love is like that rose that blooms so big and fast

2 One day your love is here, encircling my heart

3 But like those delicate petals…

4 I KNEW it would not last!

Name _____

Fill in the bubble next to the sentence that explains the <u>underlined words</u> (figure of speech).

1 **Mauricio never had any chores to do after school. He could come home and play all afternoon. His sister said, "<u>He lives a dog's life!</u>"**

(A) Mauricio has to live in the doghouse.
(B) Mauricio lives a very easy life.
(C) Mauricio can do tricks.
(D) Mauricio has a very hard life.

2 **His mom always complained that whatever she told Mark went <u>in one ear and out the other</u>. He never remembered anything she told him.**

(F) Mark didn't pay attention to what his mom told him.
(G) Mark had nothing between his ears.
(H) Mark's ears were really clean.
(J) Mark couldn't hear.

3 **Erica is always extra kind to everyone at school. Her friends say she has <u>a heart of gold</u>.**

(A) Erica's heart is heavy.
(B) Erica gives money to everyone at school.
(C) Erica is a nice person and cares for everyone.
(D) Erica has a lot of friends.

4 **Jen's office was always <u>as neat as a pin</u>.**

(F) Jen's office was full of pins.
(G) Jen's office was very messy.
(H) Jen's office was very organized.
(J) Jen's office was in a pin store.

154

1 The author capitalized the word "KNEW" in line 4 to give the poem a feeling of _____.

Ⓐ calmness and serenity

Ⓑ happiness and calmness

Ⓒ suspense and scariness

Ⓓ sadness and disappointment

2 In this poem, the ellipsis (...) are used to indicate —

Ⓕ an incomplete thought.

Ⓖ a suspenseful pause.

Ⓗ spoken words.

Ⓙ undying love.

3 The author uses the literary technique of simile to compare —

Ⓐ love and rose.

Ⓑ big and fast.

Ⓒ the author's feelings toward the loved one.

Ⓓ love and anger.

4 The lines in the poem get shorter to show the author's —

Ⓕ growing love.

Ⓖ frustration.

Ⓗ friendliness.

Ⓙ compassion.

153

Name _____

Read the student article, then answer the question.

Third graders at Jefferson School proudly displayed their insect collections at Open House on April 25.

The thirty net-wielding students had captured their insects on a very exciting field trip to Oak Canyon last month.

Each student in class displayed five insects and excitedly explained all about them to enthusiastic parents and classroom visitors.

Their teacher, Mr. Clark, said that he hopes to repeat the project next year.

1 **What is the *most* important strength of this article?**

Ⓐ Four paragraphs is a good length.

Ⓑ It tells the date of Open House.

Ⓒ The paragraphs are indented.

Ⓓ All the sentences tell about the topic.

Name _____

Fill in the bubble next to the foreign word(s) that correctly complete each sentence.

❶ She knew a lot about computers, and it was clear that she was a _____ expert in her field.

Which Latin word/saying correctly fits in the sentence above?

Ⓐ circa   Ⓒ compli

Ⓑ carpe diem   Ⓓ bona fide

❷ Suddenly, he realized he had committed yet another _____ by burping in class.

Which French word/saying correctly fits in the sentence above?

Ⓕ faux pas   Ⓗ coup de grâce

Ⓖ entre nous   Ⓙ resumé

❸ The lawyer agreed to take the _____ case; he knew he couldn't be paid.

Which Latin word/saying correctly fits in the sentence above?

Ⓐ persona non grata   Ⓒ modus operandi

Ⓑ pro bono   Ⓓ in situ

❹ Not wanting to use her real name, the author spent several hours deciding on her _____.

Which French word/saying correctly fits in the sentence above?

Ⓕ bon mot   Ⓗ nom de plume

Ⓖ carte blanche   Ⓙ trois

Name _____

Fill in the bubble next to the word (homophone) that correctly completes each sentence.

1 May I have a _____ of cake?

    Ⓐ peace

    Ⓑ piece

2 A rabbit has a short, puffy _____.

    Ⓕ tail

    Ⓖ tale

3 The boys hung up _____ coats.

    Ⓐ they're

    Ⓑ there

    Ⓒ their

4 We're going to spend a _____ in Hawaii.

    Ⓕ week

    Ⓖ weak

157

1 We've looked everywhere for the lost puppy!

The verb tense in this sentence is —

Ⓐ past perfect.　　Ⓒ future perfect.
Ⓑ present perfect.　Ⓓ none of the above

3 They'll have run four miles by the time P.E. is over.

The verb tense in this sentence is —

Ⓐ past perfect.　　Ⓒ future perfect.
Ⓑ present perfect.　Ⓓ none of the above

2 I'll have written 15 problems before recess begins.

The verb tense in this sentence is —

Ⓕ past perfect.　　Ⓗ future perfect.
Ⓖ present perfect.　Ⓙ none of the above

4 I'd walked two miles to get to the game.

The verb tense in this sentence is —

Ⓕ past perfect.　　Ⓗ future perfect.
Ⓖ present perfect.　Ⓙ none of the above

Name _____

Read the poem below. Then answer the questions that follow.

Whisky Frisky

1   Whisky, frisky,
2   Hipperty hop,
3   Up he goes
4   To the tree top!
5   Whirly, twirly,
6   Round and round
7   Down he scampers
8   To the ground.
9   Furly, curly,
10   What a tail,
11   Tall as a feather,
12   Broad as a sail.
13   Where's his supper?
14   In the shell.
15   Snappy, cracky,
16   Out it fell.

- Anonymous

❶ This poem is written in —

Ⓐ first person.

Ⓑ second person.

Ⓒ third person.

❷ What form of poetry is used in lines 1, 5, and 9?

Ⓕ alliteration

Ⓖ onomatopoeia

Ⓗ consonance

Ⓙ rhyme

1 You want to write to your best friend to tell her about your vacation. Which form of writing would be the *best* choice?

    Ⓐ personal letter   Ⓒ a poem
    Ⓑ letter to the editor   Ⓓ a report

2 You are watching the sunset over the ocean. You want to write about it. Which form of writing would be the *best* choice?

    Ⓕ personal letter   Ⓗ a poem
    Ⓖ letter to the editor   Ⓙ a report

3 You want to learn more about different sixth grade camps your school could attend. You'll present your information to the sixth grade teachers. Which form of writing would be the *best* choice for your presentation?

    Ⓐ personal letter   Ⓒ a poem
    Ⓑ letter to the editor   Ⓓ a report

4 You are upset that several stores in your city are flying U.S. flags that are torn. You want to tell people why this is wrong. Which form of writing would be the *best* choice?

    Ⓕ personal letter   Ⓗ a poem
    Ⓖ letter to the editor   Ⓙ a report

① Amber read a story about a fairy godmother who turned the princess' shoe into gold.

Amber was most likely reading a _____.

Ⓐ fairy tale   Ⓒ myth

Ⓑ tall tale   Ⓓ fable

② Kathleen read a story about a race between two animals. She learned a lesson from the story.

Kathleen was most likely reading a _____.

Ⓕ fairy tale   Ⓗ myth

Ⓖ tall tale   Ⓙ fable

③ Josué read a story about a man who tried to tunnel through a mountain faster than a machine. The man beat the machine.

Josué was most likely reading a _____.

Ⓐ fairy tale   Ⓒ myth

Ⓑ tall tale   Ⓓ fable

④ Curtis read a story about how the rain gods saved the tribe from starvation.

Curtis was most likely reading a _____.

Ⓕ fairy tale   Ⓗ myth

Ⓖ tall tale   Ⓙ fable

161

Read the passage below. Then answer the questions on the next page. You may look back at this page as you answer the questions.

Their parents told Mara and Tito, "Don't go up to the forest on the mountain. A wild man lives there!"

Tito told his sister, "I want to see that forest. I want to climb that mountain. I want to see that wild man, if there is one."

When Tito did not return to his home by nightfall, his parents began to worry. "Where can he be? Where can he be?" they asked each other. They did not ask Mara.

"I know where <u>he</u> is," she thought. "If I tell them, they will not let me go to the forest. In the morning, I'll go look for him."

Mara found it easy to follow the dirt path to the foot of the mountain. Then a different kind of trail led her even higher. There were the cast-off peelings from <u>mangoes</u> which Tito had eaten along the way. She followed footprints in the wet earth and broken branches from which he had taken switches to drag along the ground.

The forest was warm and peaceful with the scent of wildflowers and the happy songs of birds. Suddenly she heard a different kind of music. She walked on more quickly to an outcropping of rocks beside a shaded pool. There sat Tito, listening to the music of a flute played by a man she'd never seen. His dark skin glistened like polished leather beneath long, wavy black hair. His friendly brown eyes and an upward tilt to his head beckoned her closer, and she sat down beside her brother to listen.

Then she rested and refreshed herself in the pool. At last the flute player said, "Come children. I will walk with you down the mountain and see that you get home safely."

In the village that night, the surprised parents exclaimed, "That mountain man is not wild; he is kind!"

Name _____

1 **In the fourth paragraph, <u>he</u> refers to —**

Ⓐ the father.

Ⓑ the wild man.

Ⓒ Tito.

2 **From the passage you can tell that a <u>mango</u> is probably —**

Ⓕ an animal.

Ⓖ a person.

Ⓗ a candy bar.

Ⓘ a fruit or vegetable.

3 **The *mood* of the passage as Mara climbed the mountain was one of —**

Ⓐ fear.

Ⓑ dread.

Ⓒ peace and happiness.

Ⓓ anxiety.

4 **Why were the parents surprised?**

Ⓕ They were afraid Tito had run away.

Ⓖ They didn't expect to see their children again.

Ⓗ It was their anniversary.

Ⓘ The mountain man was kind, not wild.

163

Use this application to answer the questions on the next page. You may look back at this page as you answer the questions.

Junior Ballet Academy

Name _____
               Last   First   MI

Address _____
           Street   City   State   Zip Code

Phone Number _____ Age _____

Gender _____ M _____ F

Signature _____ Date _____

Person(s) to contact in case of an emergency:

Name _____

Phone Number _____

Relationship _____

Name _____

Phone Number _____

Relationship _____

PAYMENT VERIFICATION
(To be completed by staff member)

_____ cash _____ check#_____
_____ charge - type _____

1 **Which of these would correctly complete the first line on the left side of the application?**

Ⓐ Heidi M. Brown

Ⓑ Brown M. Heidi

Ⓒ Brown Heidi M.

Ⓓ Heidi Brown M.

2 **Who is supposed to complete the payment verification section of the application form?**

Ⓕ the parent

Ⓖ the child

Ⓗ both parents

Ⓙ a staff member

3 **Which of these would correctly complete the third line of the application?**

Ⓐ (714) 555-1000; 12

Ⓑ 12; (714) 555-1000

Ⓒ 55-1000; 12

Ⓓ (714) 555-1000

4 **Which of the following should you *not* list as a person to contact in case of an emergency?**

Ⓕ your mom

Ⓖ yourself

Ⓗ your doctor

Ⓙ your dad

Name _____

For each item below, choose the word that means the *same or almost the same* (synonym) as the underlined word.

1 a **polite** person

Ⓒ legal
Ⓓ courteous
Ⓔ poor
Ⓕ quiet

2 to **provide** equipment

Ⓕ promise
Ⓖ store
Ⓗ buy
Ⓘ supply

3 a **frequent** guest

Ⓒ popular
Ⓓ unexpected
Ⓔ regular
Ⓕ rude

4 to **glisten**

Ⓕ shine
Ⓖ wave
Ⓗ listen
Ⓘ mumble

Name _____

Read each sentence and look at the <u>underlined words</u>. There may be a mistake in them. Select the best answer to correct the mistake. If there is no mistake, select *correct as is*.

❶ Jimena <u>didn't have no money</u> for lunch.

   Ⓐ didn't have any money

   Ⓑ correct as is

❷ <u>Doesn't no one have money</u> to lend him?

   Ⓕ Doesn't anyone have money

   Ⓖ correct as is

❸ <u>Lina can't ever decide</u> what to wear.

   Ⓐ Lina can't never decide

   Ⓑ correct as is

❹ <u>There wasn't no one at home</u> when I got there.

   Ⓕ There wasn't anyone at home

   Ⓖ correct as is

Name _____

Fill in the bubble next to the words that correctly complete each sentence.

❶ _____ **belongs to Mr. Barrett.**

   Ⓐ The shiny new car

   Ⓑ Having bought the car

   Ⓒ Parked next to his house

   Ⓓ Saving for more than a year

❷ _____ **buries itself in the sand.**

   Ⓕ In order to hide

   Ⓖ Because it is cold

   Ⓗ When the wave goes out

   Ⓙ A clam

❸ _____ **were thrown away.**

   Ⓐ Because they were worn out

   Ⓑ Having been badly torn

   Ⓒ All torn and dirty books

   Ⓓ If no longer useful

❹ _____ **likes to sleep on my bed.**

   Ⓕ Because it is soft

   Ⓖ All night long

   Ⓗ My puppy

   Ⓙ Under the covers

Name _____

Choose the sentence below that combines all of the numbered sentences in the *best*, most concise way.

❶
1. **Jennifer wrote a story.**
2. **The story was short.**
3. **The story was humorous.**
4. **The story was about her pet duck.**

Ⓐ Jennifer wrote a short, humorous story about her pet duck.

Ⓑ Jennifer wrote a story, and the story was short and humorous about her pet duck.

Ⓒ Jennifer wrote a story about her pet duck, and it was short, and it was humorous.

Ⓓ Jennifer's pet duck is short and humorous.

❷
1. **A child was lost.**
2. **People searched for the child.**
3. **The people had searched through the night.**
4. **The people were exhausted.**

Ⓕ The people were exhausted, they searched through the night, and a child was lost.

Ⓖ A child was lost, and the people searched and through the night they were exhausted.

Ⓗ People searched for the lost child through the night, and the people were exhausted.

Ⓙ The exhausted people had searched through the night for the lost child.

Name _____

Read each sentence and look at the underlined words. There may be a mistake in them. Select the best answer to correct the mistake. If there is no mistake, select *correct as is*.

❶ **The old cabin was <u>overrun with mices</u>.**

   Ⓐ overrun with mouses

   Ⓑ overrun with mice

   Ⓒ correct as is

❷ **<u>Tran brushed his tooths</u> after lunch.**

   Ⓕ Tran brushed his teeth

   Ⓖ Tran brushed his teeths

   Ⓗ correct as is

❸ **<u>The flock of wild geese</u> flew south.**

   Ⓐ The flock of wild gooses

   Ⓑ The flock of wild geeses

   Ⓒ correct as is

❹ **<u>Many womans study</u> to become lawyers.**

   Ⓕ Many womens study

   Ⓖ Many women study

   Ⓗ correct as is

Name _____

Fill in the bubble next to the word(s) that correctly complete each sentence.

1 **Mr. Chung** _____ **the leaves.**

Ⓐ rake

Ⓑ raking

Ⓒ is raking

Ⓓ have raked

2 **Four jets** _____ **overhead.**

Ⓕ flies

Ⓖ is flying

Ⓗ flied

Ⓘ were flying

3 **Marcela and John** _____ **the car.**

Ⓐ washes

Ⓑ are washing

Ⓒ is washing

Ⓓ has washed

4 **All of the boats** _____ **out to sea.**

Ⓕ have sailed

Ⓖ is sailing

Ⓗ has sailed

Ⓘ sails

171

Read the passage below. Then answer the questions on the next page. You may look back at this page as you answer the questions.

The study of medicine offers many challenges and opportunities to the bright scholar. In college, the student takes pre-medical courses. Then, three or four more years of difficult study are followed by at least a year of internship. If the medical student decides to specialize, he or she must spend at least another year working with the kind of cases to be treated after he or she passes an examination to obtain a state license.

The person who meets these challenges successfully can choose from many fields of medicine. You may think of a doctor as one who treats you and your family when you have a cold or injure yourself. However, a doctor may be a *surgeon* (who performs operations), an *internist* (who treats patients without operating), an *ophthalmologist* (who treats the eyes), or an *otolaryngologist* (who treats the ears, nose, and throat), to name just a few. Or, a doctor may choose to work only with children, only with older people, or only with one part of the body. A dentist and a veterinarian are doctors, too!

Can you think of any career that offers so many choices?

1 The *best* title for this passage is —

Ⓐ How to Be a Good Doctor.

Ⓑ My Family Doctor.

Ⓒ Challenges and Opportunities for Doctors.

Ⓓ Colds and Injuries.

2 Which of the following steps comes *first* in becoming a doctor?

Ⓕ pre-medical courses

Ⓖ internship

Ⓗ specializing

Ⓙ obtaining a license

3 Which of the following doctors treats the eyes?

Ⓐ a surgeon

Ⓑ an internist

Ⓒ an ophthalmologist

Ⓓ an otolaryngologist

4 You know from this passage that if you choose to become a doctor, you will —

Ⓕ be rich.

Ⓖ be a surgeon.

Ⓗ have many years of study.

Ⓙ become a dentist or veterinarian.

173

Name _____

Fill in the bubble next to the word(s) that correctly complete each sentence.

1 We found sand _____ on the rocks, and in our shoes.

Ⓐ in the water

Ⓑ , in the water

Ⓒ in the water,

Ⓓ in, the water

2 Whew! What a —

Ⓕ relief?

Ⓖ relief!

Ⓗ relief"

Ⓙ relief,

3 Ashley's birthday is —

Ⓐ Aug 27, 1995.

Ⓑ Aug, 27, 1995.

Ⓒ Aug. 27 1995.

Ⓓ Aug. 27, 1995.

4 I have taken _____ lessons.

Ⓕ dancing, singing, and piano

Ⓖ dancing, singing and, piano

Ⓗ dancing, singing and piano,

Ⓙ dancing singing, and piano

❶ Choose the sentence that is the *best* topic sentence (main idea) for the paragraph.

_____ The first boat to use the canal left Buffalo, New York, on October 26 and reached New York City on November 4. The canal cost 7 million dollars, but cut travel time by one-third and greatly reduced shipping costs at that time.

Ⓐ Ships are an important form of transportation in the United States.

Ⓑ It is cheaper to send goods by truck than by ship.

Ⓒ The Erie Canal was completed and open to shipping in 1825.

Ⓓ New York City is the chief Atlantic seaport in the U.S.

❷ Choose the sentence for the blank in the paragraph that *best supports* the topic sentence.

The largest and heaviest animal living in the world today is the blue whale. It can grow to be more than 110 feet long and weigh more than 200 tons. A newborn calf (baby) measures 21-28.5 feet long and can weigh up to 3.3 tons. _____
_____

Ⓕ Killer whales have been taught to do tricks and perform for people.

Ⓖ Blue whales live in the colder seas but migrate to warmer seas for breeding.

Ⓗ A shark is a fish, but a whale is a mammal.

Ⓙ In colonial times, whaling was an important industry.

175

1 Choose the answer that correctly completes the sentence.

My shoes _____.

Ⓐ with the new shoestrings
Ⓑ a size too small
Ⓒ are too tight
Ⓓ holes in the toes

2 Choose the answer that correctly completes the sentence.

_____ hopped across the yard.

Ⓕ Taking long jumps,
Ⓖ Early in the afternoon,
Ⓗ A fat toad
Ⓙ Trying to catch a fly,

3 Choose the word that tells you *exactly* what Jim smelled.

Jim's mouth watered when he smelled the _____.

Ⓐ food   Ⓒ popcorn
Ⓑ treat   Ⓓ hot snack

4 Which of the following suggests that Bina was *nervous*?

"Yes, I'll dance with you," Bina _____.

Ⓕ stated   Ⓗ stammered
Ⓖ declared   Ⓙ shouted

Name _____

Choose the phrase that best completes each of the following sentences. (Note the <u>underlined words</u>)

❶ You may not borrow my bike because —

  Ⓐ you borrow it.

  Ⓑ you borrow my bike.

  Ⓒ you may borrow my bike.

  Ⓓ you did not promise to return it.

❷ <u>While</u> I was reading a book, —

  Ⓕ my brother was getting in trouble.

  Ⓖ and my brother was getting in trouble.

  Ⓗ but my brother was getting in trouble.

  Ⓙ or my brother was getting in trouble.

❸ <u>During</u> the movie, —

  Ⓐ and the couple talked.

  Ⓑ the couple talked.

  Ⓒ but the couple talked.

  Ⓓ or the couple talked.

❹ You may go on the trip, <u>however</u>, —

  Ⓕ and your dog may go.

  Ⓖ your dog may not go.

  Ⓗ or your dog may go.

  Ⓙ but your dog may go.

Name _____

Choose the phrase that will form a complete sentence.

❶ The mountain peak —

Ⓐ rising from the valley floor.
Ⓑ hidden by clouds.
Ⓒ is covered with snow.
Ⓓ too high to climb.

❷ Thang's mother —

Ⓕ in an office building.
Ⓖ at the hospital.
Ⓗ in college for six years.
Ⓙ is a doctor.

❸ The thunderstorm —

Ⓐ frightened the horses.
Ⓑ with lightning and rain.
Ⓒ over the distant mountains.
Ⓓ booming across the desert.

❹ The salad —

Ⓕ needs more dressing.
Ⓖ of lettuce and tomatoes.
Ⓗ for sale in the cafeteria.
Ⓙ cold and crisp in the refrigerator.

Use the dictionary entry to answer the questions below.

bark (bärk) n. **1**. the abrupt, explosive cry of a dog. **2**. *Colloq.* a cough.
3. *Botanical*. the external covering of woody stems, branches, and roots of plants.
4. *Nautical*. a sailing vessel of small size. v. **5**. to rub off the skin of: *to bark one's shins*. v. **6**. to utter in a loud and usually angry tone.

❶ Which of the above meanings fits the sentence below?

Some Indians covered canoes with <u>bark</u> from a birch tree.

Ⓐ Definition **1**

Ⓑ Definition **2**

Ⓒ Definition **3**

Ⓓ Definition **4**

❷ Which of the above meanings fits the sentence below?

The drill sergeant <u>barked</u> out orders to his troops.

Ⓕ Definition **3**

Ⓖ Definition **4**

Ⓗ Definition **5**

Ⓙ Definition **6**

Name _____

Fill in the bubble next to the word (contraction) that correctly completes each sentence.

1 Our seats were poor, and we _____ able to see well.

Ⓐ wern't
Ⓑ weren't
Ⓒ were'nt
Ⓓ wer'ent

2 _____ get better grades if you study.

Ⓕ Youl'l
Ⓖ Youw'l
Ⓗ You'l
Ⓙ You'll

3 Papa Bear said, "_____ been sleeping in my bed?"

Ⓐ Who'se
Ⓑ Who's
Ⓒ Wh'ose
Ⓓ Whoh's

4 You _____ talk with your mouth full.

Ⓕ should'nt
Ⓖ shoul'dnt
Ⓗ shouldn'ot
Ⓙ shouldn't

Name _____

Choose the words that will form one or more complete sentences.

❶ A bird's bones are _____.

Ⓐ hollow. This helps to make the bird light

Ⓑ hollow this helps to make the bird light

Ⓒ hollow. Making the bird light

Ⓓ hollow. Helps to make the bird light

❷ The kangaroo is a _____.

Ⓕ marsupial, its young in a pouch

Ⓖ marsupial. Young in a pouch

Ⓗ marsupial. Carries its young in a pouch

Ⓙ marsupial. It carries its young in a pouch

❸ Kelly's mom made fried _____.

Ⓐ chicken, I want to stay for dinner

Ⓑ chicken. I want to stay for dinner

Ⓒ chicken. Want to stay for dinner

Ⓓ chicken I want to stay

❹ Some clouds are dark and _____.

Ⓕ thick they mean that a storm is coming

Ⓖ thick, that a storm is coming

Ⓗ thick. That a storm is coming

Ⓙ thick. They mean that a storm is coming

181

Read the passage below. Then answer the questions on the next page. You may look back at this page as you answer the questions.

What is the most important invention ever developed to improve transportation? Think about this question as you read on.

As humans walked from place to place many thousands of years ago, they found ways to carry things on their shoulders, backs and heads. Then they learned to tame animals to carry things for them. You may have seen pictures of American Indians hauling <u>game</u> on a sled pulled by a pony. <u>Perhaps, many years ago, someone found it was easier to roll such a sled by putting a log under it</u>. Then someone else got the idea of cutting slices from the log and fastening those slices to the ends of a smaller log.

You have seen pictures of the covered wagons which brought the early pioneers to the western part of our country. Those wagons used the invention. The large river boats which carried the settlers and their goods up and down the Mississippi made use of it, too.

Since the development of the engine, much of our transportation has developed on roads and rails. Automobiles, railroads, subway trains, elevated trains, streetcars and buses have carried millions of passengers and tons of freight. All of these use the invention. Even present day aircraft cannot land without using it.

Think of the bicycle of today. It has no engine. A cart fastened only to an ox, buffalo or horse is still in use in many parts of the world. Both the bicycle and cart use the invention as well.

Have you figured out what the invention is?

1 **What important invention is the passage referring to?**

Ⓐ tame animals

Ⓑ the covered wagon

Ⓒ the wheel

Ⓓ the engine

2 **In this passage, <u>game</u> means —**

Ⓕ a form of amusement.

Ⓖ animals hunted for food.

Ⓗ the points needed to win.

Ⓙ a line of work.

3 **The passage *implies* that early man —**

Ⓐ was inventive.

Ⓑ was lazy.

Ⓒ traveled on a sled.

Ⓓ had no means of travel.

4 **The underlined sentence appears to be —**

Ⓕ a fact.

Ⓖ an opinion.

Read the student composition, then answer the question.

The Statue of Liberty stands in New York Harbor as a symbol of freedom. The statue was a gift of friendship to the American people from the people of France.

It was designed by a French artist named Frederic Auguste Bartholdi. After nearly ten years of work, he completed the statue in 1884. It was then ready to send to the United States.

_____

The statue's reconstruction in New York was completed in 1886. Including the pedestal on which she stands, the statue is a little over 305 feet tall. Her head is 17 feet 3 inches high, and her nose is 4 feet 6 inches long. The width of the finger nail on her index finger is 13 inches. Compare that to the size of your own fingernail, and you will get an idea of just how big she is!

1 **Suppose you wrote the composition from this outline.**

   I. **The Statue of Liberty**
      A. **Its origin**
      B. **How designed and built**
      C. **How shipped to U.S.**
      D. **Its size**

Choose the sentence needed to complete the composition according to the outline.

Ⓐ The statue was finished May 21 and presented to the U.S. on July 4, 1884.

Ⓑ The statue weighs 450,000 pounds.

Ⓒ The statue was shipped by boat in 214 packing cases.

Ⓓ The statue is a symbol of freedom.

Name _____

Read each sentence and look at the underlined words. There may be a mistake in them. Select the best answer to correct the mistake. If there is no mistake, select *correct as is*.

❶ All of the leaves have blown away.

   Ⓐ All of the leaves blowed
   Ⓑ All of the leaves blowing
   Ⓒ All of the leaves have blew
   Ⓓ correct as is

❷ Tracy did not comed to school today.

   Ⓕ did not come to school
   Ⓖ did not coming to school
   Ⓗ did not came to school
   Ⓙ correct as is

❸ Have you done your homework?

   Ⓐ Have you do
   Ⓑ Have you doing
   Ⓒ Have you did
   Ⓓ correct as is

❹ Thieves have stealed $8000 from the bank.

   Ⓕ Thieves have stolen $8000
   Ⓖ Thieves stealed $8000
   Ⓗ Thieves have stole $8000
   Ⓙ correct as is

185

Name _____

Read each set of sentences and decide if one of the <u>underlined words</u> is spelled incorrectly, or if there is *no mistake*. Choose your answer and fill in the bubble.

❶

Ⓐ The peach on the ground was <u>rotten</u>.

Ⓑ That was a <u>thoughtful</u> gift.

Ⓒ The <u>scoar</u> was tied at 4 to 4.

Ⓓ no mistake

❷

Ⓕ The knee <u>operation</u> went well.

Ⓖ There was a <u>shortage</u> of gasoline in 1979.

Ⓗ Put your feet <u>beneath</u> the desk!

Ⓙ no mistake

❸

Ⓐ They felt <u>uneasy</u> about the results.

Ⓑ The hammer is a useful <u>tule</u>.

Ⓒ The <u>iron</u> gate was rusting.

Ⓓ no mistake

❹

Ⓕ Do you know the <u>anser</u> to the question?

Ⓖ I <u>could</u> not see over their heads.

Ⓗ We ate <u>dinner</u> outside on Sunday.

Ⓙ no mistake

Name _____

Read each sentence and look at the <u>underlined words</u>. There may be a mistake in them.
Select the best answer to correct the mistake. If there is no mistake, select *correct as is*.

❶ Won't you <u>please help them</u>?

    Ⓐ please help they

    Ⓑ please help she

    Ⓒ please help he

    Ⓓ correct as is

❷ <u>My uncle and I</u> went fishing.

    Ⓕ My uncle and me

    Ⓖ My uncle and her

    Ⓗ My uncle and them

    Ⓙ correct as is

❸ <u>Tammy asked I</u> to read a story.

    Ⓐ Tammy asked me

    Ⓑ Tammy asked she

    Ⓒ Tammy asked he

    Ⓓ correct as is

❹ <u>Colin and him</u> played soccer.

    Ⓕ Colin and her

    Ⓖ Colin and he

    Ⓗ Colin and us

    Ⓙ correct as is

187

Read the passage below. Then answer the questions on the next page. You may look back at this page as you answer the questions.

There are certain rules for introducing two people who do not know each other. The main rule to remember is to name the most important person first. For instance, if a lady were meeting the Queen of England, the person introducing them would say, "Your Majesty, may I present to you Lady Macbeth." The Queen, as the ruler of the British Empire, is the most important, and so is named first. At times, you will have to decide who is the more important person.

Here are some other rules and examples:

A man is introduced to a woman. "Mrs. Moore, may I present John Smith."

A younger person is presented to an older one. "Mrs. Oldtimer, this is Helen Teenager."

If the younger person is very well known, he or she is named first. "Kid Star, I'd like you to meet my mother."

Notice in the examples that instead of "May I present to you…," you can say, "This is…," or "I'd like you to meet…."

Staying around to help get a conversation going between two people whom you have just introduced is a courtesy that is usually appreciated.

① **Choose the correct way to introduce your grandmother to your young friend.**

Ⓐ "John Friend, this is my grandmother."

Ⓑ "Grandmother, this is John Friend."

Ⓒ "Hey, John. This here's Gran."

Ⓓ "Grandma, this is a friend of mine."

② **Why is it a courtesy to stay with two people you have just introduced?**

Ⓕ so they won't argue

Ⓖ because you don't know anyone else

Ⓗ in case one forgets the other's name

Ⓙ to help them become better acquainted

③ **The author's *purpose* in writing this passage is to —**

Ⓐ entertain the reader.

Ⓑ persuade the reader.

Ⓒ inform the reader.

Ⓓ argue with the reader.

④ **In this passage, "Your Majesty" refers to —**

Ⓕ Lady Macbeth.

Ⓖ the British Empire.

Ⓗ Kid Star.

Ⓙ the Queen of England.

189

Name _____

Read each sentence and look at the <u>underlined words</u>. There may be a mistake in them. Select the best answer to correct the mistake. If there is no mistake, select *correct as is*.

1 <u>**Smoking is dangerness**</u> to your health.

    Ⓐ Smoking is dangerest
    Ⓑ Smoking is dangerous
    Ⓒ Smoking is dangerly
    Ⓓ correct as is

2 This glue is <u>**very stickous**</u>.

    Ⓕ very stickful
    Ⓖ very stickly
    Ⓗ very sticky
    Ⓙ correct as is

3 There <u>**was a wooden gate**</u> in the fence.

    Ⓐ was a woodful gate
    Ⓑ was a woodly gate
    Ⓒ was a woodable gate
    Ⓓ correct as is

4 <u>**Both teams seemed agreeful**</u> to the rules.

    Ⓕ Both teams seemed agreeable
    Ⓖ Both teams seemed agreeness
    Ⓗ Both teams seemed agreely
    Ⓙ correct as is

1 **Choose the sentence that is the *best* topic sentence (main idea) for the paragraph.**

_____ Although many efforts have been made to reduce emissions from cars and factories, smog and other pollutants pose serious threats to cities and forests. Rivers that once provided clear water for drinking and recreation are now considered hazardous due to waste discharged by factories along their banks.

Ⓐ The new models of American cars are sleek and racy this year.

Ⓑ The Mississippi River has many factories along its banks.

Ⓒ We can all learn a lesson from the animals in the forests.

Ⓓ Air and water pollution are threatening our environment.

2 **Choose the sentence for the blank in the paragraph that *best supports* the topic sentence.**

Susan and Mark wanted to build a birdhouse. They found some scraps of wood in Mark's garage. Susan's dad lent them a hammer and saw. _____ _____ They cut wood and pounded nails most of the morning. By late afternoon, their new white birdhouse hung proudly in Susan's backyard.

Ⓕ Most hammers have metal heads and wooden handles.

Ⓖ They bought nails and paint at the hardware store.

Ⓗ Susan's dad is a computer programmer for a large company.

Ⓙ Many birds fly to warmer climates when winter comes.

191

Name _____

Fill in the bubble next to the word(s) that correctly complete each sentence.

1 _____ at the ball game.

Ⓐ Had good seats

Ⓑ Lots of cheering

Ⓒ Many home runs today

Ⓓ I bought a hot dog

2 Darcy brought all of _____ newspapers for our paper drive.

Ⓕ them

Ⓖ those

Ⓗ this

Ⓙ that

3 I washed these pants twice, _____ they still look dirty.

Ⓐ until

Ⓑ or

Ⓒ but

Ⓓ nor

4 At the pet store, the _____ cages were cleaned each day.

Ⓕ animals'

Ⓖ animal's

Ⓗ animals

Name _____

Use the dictionary entry to answer the questions below.

---

bridge (brij) n. **1**. a structure spanning a river, chasm, road, or the like, and affording passage. **2**. *Nautical*. a raised platform from side to side of a ship, for the officer in charge. **3**. *Dentistry*. an artificial replacement of a missing tooth or teeth. **4**. *Anat*. the ridge or upper line of the nose. **5**. *Music*. a piece raising the strings of a musical instrument above the sounding board.

---

❶ Which of the above meanings fits the sentence below?

Kevin will need to have a <u>bridge</u> made to replace the two teeth that were knocked out when he fell.

Ⓐ Definition **1**

Ⓑ Definition **2**

Ⓒ Definition **3**

Ⓓ Definition **4**

❷ Which of the above meanings fits the sentence below?

The brave captain continued to command the ship from his position on the <u>bridge</u>.

Ⓕ Definition **1**

Ⓖ Definition **2**

Ⓗ Definition **3**

Ⓙ Definition **4**

Read the passage below. Then answer the questions on the next page. You may look back at this page as you answer the questions.

What makes a sound <u>musical</u>? If you drop a book on the floor, it makes a sound. But is that music? Of course not. What makes some musical compositions become classics? Is it because they are played a lot on the radio? Not necessarily.

Music is made when a voice or instrument is made to vibrate, producing a tone that is usually pleasant to hear. The tone may be at a high or low pitch, or many tones may be combined to make harmony. A pattern of tones (notes) is called the melody or tune. You usually remember the tune of a song more easily than the words. The rhythm or beat follows a pattern of accented and unaccented tones. Whether fast or slow, it is called the tempo.

Three hundred years after the birth of Johann Sebastian Bach, his compositions are still played and considered classics. He was an accomplished performer on the organ and harpsichord before the piano or radio were invented. He wrote many exercises which helped his pupils become better performers and which piano students still practice today.

194

Name _____

1 To make harmony, —

ⓐ many tones are combined.

ⓑ patterns are accented.

ⓒ instruments vibrate.

ⓓ a high pitch is used.

2 In the word <u>musical</u>, the <u>al</u> makes the word mean —

Ⓕ full of music.

Ⓖ without music.

Ⓗ less music.

Ⓘ before music.

3 You can tell from this passage that Johann Sebastian Bach —

ⓐ is still alive.

ⓑ played the radio.

ⓒ played the piano.

ⓓ was a great composer.

4 The author's *purpose* in writing this passage is —

Ⓕ to persuade the reader.

Ⓖ to inform the reader.

Ⓗ to create a picture.

Ⓘ to describe a scene.

Name _____

Fill in the bubble next to the word (plural) that correctly completes each sentence.

1 Mr. Shea spent two _____ in the hospital.

Ⓐ weekies

Ⓑ week

Ⓒ weeks

2 Six _____ were born last spring.

Ⓕ calf

Ⓖ calfs

Ⓗ calves

3 There are many good _____ in this book.

Ⓐ stories

Ⓑ storys

Ⓒ story

4 Two _____ were hurt in the accident.

Ⓕ womens

Ⓖ women

Ⓗ woman

1 Which of the following suggests that Reza was *happy*?

"I finished my book report!" Reza shouted —

Ⓐ loudly.
Ⓑ joyfully.
Ⓒ sharply.
Ⓓ shyly.

2 Which of the following suggests that Jan was trying to be *helpful*?

"Take smaller steps," Jan —

Ⓕ cried.
Ⓖ begged.
Ⓗ threatened.
Ⓙ suggested.

3 Which of the following suggests that Martin was *very upset*?

"I lost my lunch money," Martin —

Ⓐ wailed.
Ⓑ murmured.
Ⓒ said.
Ⓓ replied.

4 Which of the following suggests that Rosa was *respected* by her classmates?

All her classmates _____ Rosa.

Ⓕ laughed at
Ⓖ ate lunch with
Ⓗ borrowed money from
Ⓙ listened to

Name _____

Fill in the bubble next to the answer that correctly completes each sentence.

❶ To find maps of the different countries in Africa, you should look in —

- Ⓐ a dictionary.
- Ⓑ a library catalog.
- Ⓒ an atlas.
- Ⓓ a newspaper.

❷ To find a local store that sells bicycles, you should look in —

- Ⓕ a magazine.
- Ⓖ the telephone directory yellow pages.
- Ⓗ an encyclopedia.
- Ⓙ a library catalog.

❸ To find the history of China, you should look in —

- Ⓐ a dictionary.
- Ⓑ an encyclopedia.
- Ⓒ an atlas.
- Ⓓ a newspaper.

❹ To find the weight of the largest watermelon ever grown, you should look in a —

- Ⓕ science book.
- Ⓖ world record book.
- Ⓗ dictionary.
- Ⓙ magazine.

Name _____

Choose the sentence below that combines all of the numbered sentences in the *best*, most concise way.

❶
1. **Mike ordered salad.**
2. **Janice ordered salad.**
3. **Estella had soup.**
4. **Tony had soup.**

Ⓐ Mike ordered salad and Janice ordered salad and Estella had soup and Tony had soup.

Ⓑ Mike ordered salad, Janice ordered salad, Estella had soup, and Tony had soup.

Ⓒ Mike and Janice ordered salad, Estella had soup, and Tony had soup.

Ⓓ Mike and Janice ordered salad, but Estella and Tony had soup.

❷
1. **Ants are insects.**
2. **Bees are insects.**
3. **Black widows are spiders.**
4. **Tarantulas are spiders.**

Ⓕ Ants and bees are insects, black widows are spiders, tarantulas are spiders.

Ⓖ Ants and bees are insects, but black widows and tarantulas are spiders.

Ⓗ Ants are insects, bees are insects, black widows are spiders, tarantulas are spiders.

Ⓙ Ants are insects, and bees are insects, and black widows are spiders, and tarantulas are spiders.

Name _____

Choose the words that will form one or more complete sentences.

❶ It rained very hard _____.

   Ⓐ last night. Making driving dangerous

   Ⓑ last night, making driving dangerous

   Ⓒ last night, is making driving dangerous

   Ⓓ last night. Because driving is dangerous

❷ Thursday is Amber's _____.

   Ⓕ birthday, we will have a party

   Ⓖ birthday. Will have a party

   Ⓗ birthday, going to have a party

   Ⓙ birthday. We will have a party

❸ Caleb borrowed my _____.

   Ⓐ jacket. He had left his at home

   Ⓑ jacket he had left his at home

   Ⓒ jacket. Left his at home

   Ⓓ jacket, his at home

❹ Paris, the capital of _____.

   Ⓕ France, a beautiful city

   Ⓖ France, is a beautiful city

   Ⓗ France. It is a beautiful city

   Ⓙ France, being a beautiful city

Name _____

Choose the answer that *best* completes each sentence. (Note the <u>underlined words</u>)

❶ <u>Although</u> it snowed all night, —

    Ⓐ it did not snow.
    Ⓑ it was not deep enough for skiing.
    Ⓒ the snow was cold.
    Ⓓ the weatherman predicted snow.

❷ I looked everywhere, <u>but</u> —

    Ⓕ I wanted to look.
    Ⓖ I couldn't find my lunch money.
    Ⓗ I looked under the bed.
    Ⓙ my mother looked everywhere.

❸ <u>Until</u> the bird learns to fly, —

    Ⓐ it will learn to fly.
    Ⓑ it learns to fly slowly.
    Ⓒ it will fly away.
    Ⓓ it will stay in the nest.

❹ You will feel better <u>if</u> —

    Ⓕ you take your medicine.
    Ⓖ you are sick.
    Ⓗ you feel worse.
    Ⓙ you don't feel well.

201

Read the passage below. Then answer the questions on the next page. You may look back at this page as you answer the questions.

Using the **scientific method** can help in solving many problems. There are four steps:

First, **state the problem**, something you wonder about. (*Are these paper clips made of steel?*)

Next, **form a <u>hypothesis</u>**; that is, take an educated guess making use of what you already know. (*They don't feel like plastic, and they look like steel. I know a magnet will pick up steel. If a magnet picks up these paper clips, I will know they are probably steel.*)

Third, **experiment and observe**; that is, do something and watch what happens. (*Using a magnet, try to pick up the paper clips.*)

Finally, **draw some conclusions**. (*The magnet picked up the paper clips so they are probably made of steel.*)

Notice that the conclusion drawn was stated as "probably" true. You may have to do many other experiments and make careful records to show how and what you did before you believe that you have proved that an idea is true.

Using the scientific method can help in solving personal problems, too. Suppose you wonder whether or not you should exercise. That is step one. Step two, say whether you think it is helpful or harmful. Three, observe; learn what happens when people do exercise. Four, draw some conclusions for yourself.

Write down these four steps to the scientific method. Memorize them and use them. That's the scientific way of problem solving.

Name _____

1 This passage *mainly* tells —

  Ⓐ how to use the scientific method to solve problems.
  Ⓑ how to do science experiments.
  Ⓒ why or why not to exercise.
  Ⓓ how to form a hypothesis.

2 From this passage, you can tell that a <u>hypothesis</u> is —

  Ⓕ an experiment.
  Ⓖ a conclusion.
  Ⓗ a proven fact.
  Ⓙ an educated guess.

3 *"Will electricity travel through plastic?"* is an example of —

  Ⓐ stating a problem.
  Ⓑ forming a hypothesis.
  Ⓒ experimenting and observing.
  Ⓓ drawing some conclusions.

4 Why should you do more than one experiment before you draw some conclusions?

  Ⓕ Experiments are fun to do.
  Ⓖ The more evidence you have, the better your conclusions will be.
  Ⓗ You will get a better grade.

203

Read the student article, then answer the question.

A devastating flash flood hit Rockford City on September 5. It hit about 5:30 p.m.

It caused severe damage to the bridge over Whitefork River at the south end of town. It stranded people on both sides of the river for more than four hours.

It raged through the river channel as heavy storm clouds dropped some 2-3 inches of rain in two and one-half hours.

It caused an estimated $500,000 in damage.

It was the worst flash flood to hit this area in over forty years.

❶ **What would you change to *most improve* this student's article?**

Ⓐ Avoid so many details.

Ⓑ Change the name of the river.

Ⓒ Write more paragraphs.

Ⓓ Combine some sentences, and avoid so many uses of "it."

Page _____

A

1. Ⓐ Ⓑ Ⓒ Ⓓ Ⓔ
2. Ⓕ Ⓖ Ⓗ Ⓙ Ⓚ
3. Ⓐ Ⓑ Ⓒ Ⓓ Ⓔ
4. Ⓕ Ⓖ Ⓗ Ⓙ Ⓚ

Page _____

B

1. Ⓐ Ⓑ Ⓒ Ⓓ Ⓔ
2. Ⓕ Ⓖ Ⓗ Ⓙ Ⓚ
3. Ⓐ Ⓑ Ⓒ Ⓓ Ⓔ
4. Ⓕ Ⓖ Ⓗ Ⓙ Ⓚ

Page _____

C

1. Ⓐ Ⓑ Ⓒ Ⓓ Ⓔ
2. Ⓕ Ⓖ Ⓗ Ⓙ Ⓚ
3. Ⓐ Ⓑ Ⓒ Ⓓ Ⓔ
4. Ⓕ Ⓖ Ⓗ Ⓙ Ⓚ

Page _____

D

1. Ⓐ Ⓑ Ⓒ Ⓓ Ⓔ
2. Ⓕ Ⓖ Ⓗ Ⓙ Ⓚ
3. Ⓐ Ⓑ Ⓒ Ⓓ Ⓔ
4. Ⓕ Ⓖ Ⓗ Ⓙ Ⓚ

Page _____

E

1. Ⓐ Ⓑ Ⓒ Ⓓ Ⓔ
2. Ⓕ Ⓖ Ⓗ Ⓙ Ⓚ
3. Ⓐ Ⓑ Ⓒ Ⓓ Ⓔ
4. Ⓕ Ⓖ Ⓗ Ⓙ Ⓚ

Page _____

F

1. Ⓐ Ⓑ Ⓒ Ⓓ Ⓔ
2. Ⓕ Ⓖ Ⓗ Ⓙ Ⓚ
3. Ⓐ Ⓑ Ⓒ Ⓓ Ⓔ
4. Ⓕ Ⓖ Ⓗ Ⓙ Ⓚ

Page _____

G

1. Ⓐ Ⓑ Ⓒ Ⓓ Ⓔ
2. Ⓕ Ⓖ Ⓗ Ⓙ Ⓚ
3. Ⓐ Ⓑ Ⓒ Ⓓ Ⓔ
4. Ⓕ Ⓖ Ⓗ Ⓙ Ⓚ

Page _____

H

1. Ⓐ Ⓑ Ⓒ Ⓓ Ⓔ
2. Ⓕ Ⓖ Ⓗ Ⓙ Ⓚ
3. Ⓐ Ⓑ Ⓒ Ⓓ Ⓔ
4. Ⓕ Ⓖ Ⓗ Ⓙ Ⓚ

Page _____

I

1. Ⓐ Ⓑ Ⓒ Ⓓ Ⓔ
2. Ⓕ Ⓖ Ⓗ Ⓙ Ⓚ
3. Ⓐ Ⓑ Ⓒ Ⓓ Ⓔ
4. Ⓕ Ⓖ Ⓗ Ⓙ Ⓚ

Page _____

J

1. Ⓐ Ⓑ Ⓒ Ⓓ Ⓔ
2. Ⓕ Ⓖ Ⓗ Ⓙ Ⓚ
3. Ⓐ Ⓑ Ⓒ Ⓓ Ⓔ
4. Ⓕ Ⓖ Ⓗ Ⓙ Ⓚ

Page _____

K

1. Ⓐ Ⓑ Ⓒ Ⓓ Ⓔ
2. Ⓕ Ⓖ Ⓗ Ⓙ Ⓚ
3. Ⓐ Ⓑ Ⓒ Ⓓ Ⓔ
4. Ⓕ Ⓖ Ⓗ Ⓙ Ⓚ

Page _____

L

1. Ⓐ Ⓑ Ⓒ Ⓓ Ⓔ
2. Ⓕ Ⓖ Ⓗ Ⓙ Ⓚ
3. Ⓐ Ⓑ Ⓒ Ⓓ Ⓔ
4. Ⓕ Ⓖ Ⓗ Ⓙ Ⓚ

Page _____

A
1. Ⓐ Ⓑ Ⓒ Ⓓ Ⓔ
2. Ⓕ Ⓖ Ⓗ Ⓙ Ⓚ
3. Ⓐ Ⓑ Ⓒ Ⓓ Ⓔ
4. Ⓕ Ⓖ Ⓗ Ⓙ Ⓚ

Page _____

B
1. Ⓐ Ⓑ Ⓒ Ⓓ Ⓔ
2. Ⓕ Ⓖ Ⓗ Ⓙ Ⓚ
3. Ⓐ Ⓑ Ⓒ Ⓓ Ⓔ
4. Ⓕ Ⓖ Ⓗ Ⓙ Ⓚ

Page _____

C
1. Ⓐ Ⓑ Ⓒ Ⓓ Ⓔ
2. Ⓕ Ⓖ Ⓗ Ⓙ Ⓚ
3. Ⓐ Ⓑ Ⓒ Ⓓ Ⓔ
4. Ⓕ Ⓖ Ⓗ Ⓙ Ⓚ

Page _____

D
1. Ⓐ Ⓑ Ⓒ Ⓓ Ⓔ
2. Ⓕ Ⓖ Ⓗ Ⓙ Ⓚ
3. Ⓐ Ⓑ Ⓒ Ⓓ Ⓔ
4. Ⓕ Ⓖ Ⓗ Ⓙ Ⓚ

Page _____

E
1. Ⓐ Ⓑ Ⓒ Ⓓ Ⓔ
2. Ⓕ Ⓖ Ⓗ Ⓙ Ⓚ
3. Ⓐ Ⓑ Ⓒ Ⓓ Ⓔ
4. Ⓕ Ⓖ Ⓗ Ⓙ Ⓚ

Page _____

F
1. Ⓐ Ⓑ Ⓒ Ⓓ Ⓔ
2. Ⓕ Ⓖ Ⓗ Ⓙ Ⓚ
3. Ⓐ Ⓑ Ⓒ Ⓓ Ⓔ
4. Ⓕ Ⓖ Ⓗ Ⓙ Ⓚ

Page _____

G
1. Ⓐ Ⓑ Ⓒ Ⓓ Ⓔ
2. Ⓕ Ⓖ Ⓗ Ⓙ Ⓚ
3. Ⓐ Ⓑ Ⓒ Ⓓ Ⓔ
4. Ⓕ Ⓖ Ⓗ Ⓙ Ⓚ

Page _____

H
1. Ⓐ Ⓑ Ⓒ Ⓓ Ⓔ
2. Ⓕ Ⓖ Ⓗ Ⓙ Ⓚ
3. Ⓐ Ⓑ Ⓒ Ⓓ Ⓔ
4. Ⓕ Ⓖ Ⓗ Ⓙ Ⓚ

Page _____

I
1. Ⓐ Ⓑ Ⓒ Ⓓ Ⓔ
2. Ⓕ Ⓖ Ⓗ Ⓙ Ⓚ
3. Ⓐ Ⓑ Ⓒ Ⓓ Ⓔ
4. Ⓕ Ⓖ Ⓗ Ⓙ Ⓚ

Page _____

J
1. Ⓐ Ⓑ Ⓒ Ⓓ Ⓔ
2. Ⓕ Ⓖ Ⓗ Ⓙ Ⓚ
3. Ⓐ Ⓑ Ⓒ Ⓓ Ⓔ
4. Ⓕ Ⓖ Ⓗ Ⓙ Ⓚ

Page _____

K
1. Ⓐ Ⓑ Ⓒ Ⓓ Ⓔ
2. Ⓕ Ⓖ Ⓗ Ⓙ Ⓚ
3. Ⓐ Ⓑ Ⓒ Ⓓ Ⓔ
4. Ⓕ Ⓖ Ⓗ Ⓙ Ⓚ

Page _____

L
1. Ⓐ Ⓑ Ⓒ Ⓓ Ⓔ
2. Ⓕ Ⓖ Ⓗ Ⓙ Ⓚ
3. Ⓐ Ⓑ Ⓒ Ⓓ Ⓔ
4. Ⓕ Ⓖ Ⓗ Ⓙ Ⓚ